Enjoy Reading!

Jules Dany

Oyster Bay
& Other Short Stories

JULES S. DAMJI

Bloomington, IN Milton Keynes, UK

authorHOUSE®

"The real voyage of discovery consists not in seeking new landscapes but in having new eyes."

Marcel Proust

Contents

Author's Note   xiii

Mango Tree   1
Race Drivers   10
Caretaker   24
The Middlemen   45
The Marxist and His Sister   128
A Household Divided   156
Oyster Bay   181
Freedom Fighter   188
Family Reunion   218

Glossary   255

Author's Note

The stories and characters in this collection are purely fictional. Any resemblance to names, or people in real life, is merely coincidental. The references to presidential and religious figures should be taken in purely fictional context. But the setting, the landscape, the streets, the smells, the Oyster Bay beach area, the residential Asian district of Upanga with the dwellings by the mosque — where some of the characters live in these stories — and the larger part of Dar es Salaam — known to many endearingly as Dar — are real.

Of course, much has changed since the mid 1960s and the decade of the 1970s, a time of immense political and social upheaval in the country that marked and defined many people's lives.

It is during these times of innocence, turmoil and uncertainty that the social ethos of the immigrant Asian community, undeniably part of the historical landscape of Eastern and Southern Africa, is explored. The yearning sentiments in these stories of a sense of loss of history slipping away with death of each generation are shared by me; the rest is purely fictional.

Through out these narratives, the fictional narrator's strong desire of self discovery, a journey to illuminate his past, which ultimately inspires him to write them, is expressed sometimes with cool detachment and scrutiny, sometimes with painful sorrow. The narrator's view point changes over the course of time: from a young pubescent boy (*Mango Tree* and *Race Drivers*) to a growing adult. Not all stories are narrated by the same fictional voice, but the underlying theme of self-discovery pervades throughout them, the desire of self-expression, and the impetus to write. Collectively, they embody a small slice of history, a moment of time in these characters' lives, albeit fictional yet set in settings once real.

Jules Damji
07/23/2006

Oyster Bay & Other Short Stories

Mango Tree

A long time ago, a mango tree was planted where I now live, nobody knows how long ago, before I was born, even before my grandparents' time, and certainly before a community of Indians established a residence in this small patch of land in Upanga, a mainly residential area north of Dar es Salaam, our old city and a historical port, a vestibule for journeys into the heartland of Africa.

I am fourteen years old, and I live with my parents and two older brothers in the first row of identical, two-story, white flats, with a simple and small, treeless courtyard in the front of the house, and a small untidy garden in the back with a banana plant and some shrubbery. Ours is flat number seven. Each row has thirteen flats, each connected by a shared wall, and altogether, there are seven rows. At the end of the seventh row is our grand mosque, with water fountains and well-kept gardens. The mango tree is midway between the first and second row of flats.

During the day from our living room window, I can see the tree's majestic presence, extending its green canopy and low, sturdy, matted branches across the breadth of the dirt road that divides the rows of flats. When the sea breeze from the Indian Ocean makes its way inwards, cutting through its lush foliage, it transports a fresh mango smell into our flats through the open windows or doorways. On dark nights, its exposed and convoluted roots gave it an ominous and haunted look — as though African spirits from inhabitants of this patch of dispossessed land, now dead, came to life.

For many, it provided shade from the unforgiving afternoon sun after a game of football or cricket. Its ripe mango fruits provided a juicy snack; its unmistakable landmark was a meeting spot for African nannies and servants. The low, sturdy branches were ideal for a makeshift swing with some rope and a discarded tire, and the enclosing canopy provided a gathering place for old and young during the day and at night, a resting place for night-time watchmen, or *askaris*. It was a shady parking place for some households who were stupid enough to park their cars underneath it, only to find dents from ripe mangoes splashed on their bonnets and windscreens.

On Sunday mornings, Hindu barbers from town set up shop under its inviting canopy and cut children's hair and shave neighborhood men's beards. In the afternoon, after all the Hindu barbers departed, the African grocers — from the nearby African towns of Kinondoni and Msasani — unrolled their knitted mats and displayed their goods, mainly fruits and vegetables from their home gardens, for sale. It was like a small bazaar of sorts, where household women gathered to gossip about the goings-on in the community while buying weekly groceries. It was always festive, never boring.

And before our mosque was built, evening prayers were held beneath its canopy. The mango tree was part of our existence, part of our community, yet nobody knew what was there before or how the tree came to be, or who lived on this patch of land, now exclusively for a sect of Indian Muslims. We assumed the tree's existence but never questioned its origin, like everything around us. We all accepted, willingly and blindly, what it offered. It had assumed a life of a giving tree.

Young couples carved love hearts into the trunk; others marked their names and of their secret loves: "A was here – 4/6/1957," "S loves M," or "J+S forever." Such engravings on its bark evoked excitement and curiosity, something to wonder about.

One day, I got out of school early. I came home and did my lessons on a table beside a window in full view of the tree. A government Land Rover from the local city council drove up the dirt road and pulled up under the tree. Four men, two Africans in short khakis and white shirts jumped out from the back, while a white man and an Indian man stepped outside from the front seats. They walked around the wide tree trunk, looked up at its height, and exchanged some words, pointing and tracing its flowing branches.

An excited Indian woman, a new bride from India clad in a bright sari on this hot African day, emerged from her doorway and walked briskly across her front courtyard to greet the officials. The end of her pleated sari dragged loose dust, and her Indian slippers flapped and kicked puffs of dirt behind her. They exchanged greetings and engaged in conversation as if she was aware what official business the team of men was commissioned for.

The white man broke off from the group and walked to the Land Rover. He returned with a yellow piece of paper in one hand and a small hammer in the other. He nailed the yellow notice with black letters onto the wide tree trunk.

Shortly, the officials left, leaving the new Indian bride under the tree.

The Indian woman smiled maliciously and walked joyfully back to her house. Her oily, long dark hair, singly plaited, swung on her exposed back just below her sari's blouse, like a clock's pendulum; her gait exuded purpose and accomplishment.

I did not have to read the notice. I knew what it was.

"Ma, Mama Khelele has done it!" I called out.

Mother emerged from the kitchen, wearing her usual African *kitenge* dress, always discolored and soiled around the waist perhaps from habit of constantly wiping her hands on it instead of using a rag or wearing an apron.

"Done what?"

"She has ordered the city officials to cut down the tree!"

"How do you know?"

I explained.

We nervously and solemnly walked up to the tree, and read the notice:

> *The local city officials of Upanga District Council regard this mango tree a hazard to the public and the residents of these rows of flats. We shall begin the task of cutting the tree down in three phases: First, we shall cut down all the branches. Second, we will cut the trunk in stages, and finally, we will uproot the trunk.*
>
> *We expect full cooperation from residents of these flats to abide by rules stated in city code section 5. The process will begin 5th February 1968 at 8:00 AM and will continue for at least one week. We expect this operation to be safe, but we require that you adhere to the safety instructions that will follow in the post shortly.*

All the wood from the tree will be sold to Mattil Lal
Industries, and proceeds from the sale will be donated
to the Upanga City Workers Fund.

Yours Truly,
Chief Officer Clyde Johnson
Upanga City Works Council
5ᵗʰ January, 1968

"That woman has been trouble since she arrived from India!" said Mother, exasperated. She added, "Everything here has changed, eh?"

"Yes, Ma. Everything."

She put her arm around me, consoling me, and we walked in silence back to our house. I looked back before entering my house and saw others reading the notice, talking among themselves and shaking their heads side to side with palms of their hands on each cheek, a typical Indian gesture of disbelief.

Mama Khelele was the new bride from India and my friend Amins's step-mother. He lived in the flat two doors down from us with his two older sisters. Amin's mother died during his birth, I was told, but he was raised by his two sisters and an aunt from Congo who visited frequently. His father, a stern-looking colonial, always dressed in white shirt and white trousers, worked as a clerk at a British shipping company in the city center. His father was renowned for his bad temper and capacity to drink, and Amin and his sisters were always in good manners with him about the house.

A few years after the tragedy, his father went one day to India and returned with a new bride half his age. Nine months later, Amin had a step-brother, Moez. Nothing was the same after the new arrivals.

It started with Amin. His step-mother banned him from playing with us. Then she restrained us from playing cricket and football in the street near her house by hiring a day time *askari* to guard her courtyard. If ever a ball should fall from an over-zealous kicker inside her courtyard, the *askari* was instructed to take it and plunge a knife into it in front of us. Many of my playmates witnessed their prized items burst in front of their weeping eyes.

More than once, she yelled and screamed profanities at us in Hindi (which nobody understood) for disobeying her instructions or demands. But we were not the only unlucky ones. Her treatment extended to her household members: Amin, his sisters, their father, and the servant, but never Moez, her child, for he was still young.

Occasionally, she would brandish broom sticks to street hawkers, complaining that noise from the Sunday African fruit sellers outside the mango tree deprived her child of his afternoon nap. The fruit vendors would be chased away.

Out of mockery, the African hawkers named her "Mama Khelele," a Swahili term for a screaming and ranting mother. We, too, referred to her by that name.

She fought and squawked with everyone in the neighborhood: the milkman, the Hindu barber who cut her son's hair, the house servant, the fruit and vegetable hawkers, the nannies, and the other women in the neighboring flats. Her reputation as a troublemaker followed her everywhere: into the mosque, at school with teachers, and in town with Indian shop owners.

One Sunday afternoon, during the open market under the mango tree, she argued with a fruit seller who sold her a delicious mango. She claimed the mango was from our tree and refused to pay. When the African seller demanded the money, she slapped him.

The African fruit seller, furious but restrained, said to her, "*Weh mama weh mshenzi:* you have offended the night spirits of this mango tree. You will regret this moment!"

By one account, early next morning — before the morning Muslim prayers in our mosque at the end of the rows of flats — the African fruit seller's village witchdoctor performed the African ritual to cast a spell on her. He left a beheaded chicken in her courtyard, with bougainvillea flowers, a small branch of the mango tree with a festering rotten fruit at its end, and a coconut husk, all encircled with smooth, marble-sized stones covered in the freshly slaughtered chicken blood.

We knew what it was; we had heard horror stories about African magic from people in the interior, from people across from the islands of Kilwa, Pemba, and Zanzibar. It terrified us when our grandparents from the islands narrated ghost stories about these magical spells by the witchdoctors.

With time, Mama Khelele's rants grew maddening. Perhaps the African witchcraft spell had possessed her, doing its magic. Perhaps because she did not know the ways of this land, its people, its language, and her behavior was out of frustration and rejection in her new life. Or perhaps, in the end, she came to believe what the African fruit seller told her, and her rants progressively turned into threats of commissioning the local authorities to cut down the mango tree.

She complained to her husband that she could not sleep at night because the tapering ends of the branches came to life at night, extending their tentacles through the barred window into the bedroom poking and tickling her, and caressing the inside of her thighs.

Race Drivers

The Panjwanis and the Remtullahs lived in the flats near the grand mosque, located along the bending Upanga Road that lead to grander suburbia of Oyster Bay and lowly African districts of Kinondoni.

Both households had an uncommon bond: Nizar Panjwani and Zully Remtullah had married each other's sister. Apart from this familial relationship, they had a common passion for adventure and fast cars. Their unwavering love of racing cars from childhood into their adult life transformed both into celebrity race drivers.

As a pair, they competed in the world-renowned East African Safari Motor Rally — a dirt road race spanning three adjoining countries. The race was held each year during the short rainy season, making the routes treacherous, muddy and unforgiving. But their affinity for the unusual — discouraged within the community because it was not enterprising — was the source of both envy and pride.

A few weeks before the event, a drawing is held to determine at which one of the major East African cities

— Nairobi, Dar, or Kampala — the first leg would begin, the second leg would end, and which would be the finish line. It created much excitement and anticipation among the followers, like the euphoria and anxiety before a long-awaited football game.

European media personnel descended upon the cities; hotels and restaurants were crowded; bars were packed; and among the wealthy, bets abounded. The city transformed itself into a European tropical resort, a spectacle obligingly entertained by the locals.

This time around, Dar won the first leg from which ninety-eight registered cars would commence their grueling 2600-mile journey across the three East African neighboring countries: first, through treacherous and muddy roads, inland east towards Dodoma; then north, past Mwanza; and then to Kampala where the first leg would end. The last leg would stretch westwards, cutting across the Rift Valley, through Nyeri and Nakuru, then down to Nairobi where only a handful of battered cars would cross the checkered flag.

It is a grueling and demanding run.

Each Sunday morning, our mother treats my father, my two brothers and I to an English breakfast: cornflakes, sausage, eggs, imported cheese, toast, marmalade, and tea. So we longed for Sundays. But midway through one sumptuous meal, I heard a familiar voice outside.

"Jamil, Jamil, man, come outside!" I recognized the voice. It was Paku, who lived in the flat across the street.

My brother, Amin, seated across the table from me asked, "Why does he always shout from outside? Why can't he knock the door or ring the bell?"

All these years I have known Paku, he has never knocked or rang the bell. He would shout from the courtyard, as if summoning for prayers, like the *jamat bhais* of our mosque for early morning and evening prayers.

Paku was always vociferous and crass. I have never heard him whisper or speak softly. I often wondered whether he had hearing problems, or if part of his family was deaf, for they all were loud, as if they were perpetually arguing. We could hear his father shout at his mom and she would reply in kind.

"Ah, bana, bring my tea!"

"Why are clothes not ironed?"

"Are we going to the mosque?"

These blusterous broadcasts continued during the morning hours before his father parted for work, during the day when the mother instructed the house servant with chores, in the evening during dinner conversation, and at night, while the family played cards. The immediate neighbors knew all the family secrets.

Paku clamored, "Jamil, man, come on. Look at the car!"

Reluctantly — and to shut him up before my brother Amin screamed at him — I walked to window and saw Paku just beyond the courtyard in his white shirt and oversized khaki shorts — our school uniform — from under which his bandy legs looked like two sticks.

"What?"

"Look, man, see the car?" he pointed up the street, where the Remtullahs lived.

Outside the Remtullah's flat, a crowd had gathered and encircled a car.

Excited and curious, I rushed out, deserting the cherished English breakfast, and Paku and I briskly walked towards the crowd under our famous mango tree.

It was partly cloudy outside, a sure sign of a mid-afternoon equatorial downpour. The clouds appeared gray and laden with moisture gathered from the vast Indian Ocean, which was just a few minutes walk from the rows of flats.

Paku lead the way into the crowd, shoving and parting a couple of older Indian men, who smiled and made way for us to the front of the line.

There it was: a shimmering, white Saab, two-door sports coupe model. Its front was protected with a sturdy iron mesh grill, which guarded its owl-like headlights from flying debris. Midway on the top bar of the grill were two sets of powerful spotlights with protective iron mesh. At each corner — where the slick white bonnet met the windshield — were mounted two fog spotlights for night navigation in all weather.

Rain and fog at night are common in the high country, where visibility is dismal. But when all car lights are turned on at night, it would illuminate the dark African roadways and scare any nocturnal creatures off the road.

A black, painted stripe, a foot wide, ran from the bonnet along the top of the car and continued along the trunk. On each side of the car door, a black, solid circle with number "6" was painted in white. It gave the car a zebra motif. All over the car, small stickers advertised various companies' products: spark plugs, tires, motor oils. On both rear side windows, a Tanzanian flag sticker marked its pride.

Inside, the car was stripped to the minimum: only two front bucket leather seats with safety belts; a dashboard littered with incomprehensible dials, gauges, and meters; and a small steering wheel. A massive bar ran along the inside top and side of the car like a cage, protecting its drivers from being squashed in a rollover.

All around us, we heard the elders muttering and speculating about what gadgets were used for what, how

Around 9:00 AM, just before send off, the crowd grew ecstatic as a voice crackled on a loud speaker attached to the trees above us. The preliminary, ceremonial speeches by dignitaries bored us. Finally, we heard car engines roar. Many around us had brought their portable radios so we could follow along as the BBC African Service commentators were broadcasting the event live.

We heard a list of names and car numbers being positioned for takeoff. None registered. Most were foreigners: Italians, French, Germans, Japanese, British, and Scandinavians.

Oddly, there were no Africans. They were let in later in the years for reasons typical of post-independence politics: many did not have cars or were too poor to own them. Sustenance and survival were their priorities, so they enjoyed car racing vicariously; it was a foreign sport for Africans, many thought, but not for long.

The first car — a Peugeot 404, number 25 — passed us, its engine roaring as the car driver downshifted gears to take a turn before speeding off. Then, we watched as a few more made their way past the cheering crowd. Burt Shakeland's car — Peugeot 404, number 15 — was greeted with much enthusiasm because he enlisted himself as a Tanzanian resident even though he was English, a colonial. After a few more, the much-hated Kenyan, Joginder Singh, in his Datsun coupe, made his appearance. He was greeted with cheers — and jeers.

At last, the moment for which we all came to watch and support: The "African Zebra" entered the road, and the local crowd exploded in joyous ovation, waving their national flags and setting aside the vast racial and economic differences. Here were two Tanzanians competing against the best of the world.

After the last car sped off, we walked back home along Ocean Road. The decayed kelp and dead fish scent wafted from the Indian Ocean.

We did not have television sets, so the rally progress was broadcast every couple of hours on the local station. The next report was not until 6:00 PM.

I sat anxiously next to the radio. My brothers were a bit older and curbed their enthusiasm.

"Jamil, Jamil!" came the familiar loud cry from outside. My brothers gave me the disdainful look and rolled their eyes.

I went to the window.

"What?"

"You listening to the report, *bana*? It will be on in few minutes. Can I come inside?" Paku asked, stuttering a little.

"He is not coming in here!" said Amin.

"Why not?"

"I want to listen to the report, not his loud mouth!" declared Amin.

"Well, I will tell him to be quiet."

"If he opens his mouth, I am going to send him home!" Amin warned me.

I signaled Paku to come over.

Paku raced in, crashed into the sofa, bounced off, and tumbled on the floor. He always crashed or stumbled into things, and it never bothered him, no matter how hard he was hurt. Paku was awkward in all ways.

"Are you okay?"

"Yes, man!" declared Paku.

He casually brushed his knee caps which appeared bruised. As always after these clumsy incidents, Paku seemed unfazed, his face blank, showing no sign of hurt or shame.

"Turn it on! Turn it on, man!" he said loudly.

Amin gave me his annoyed look, and reached for the radio dial.

A crisp English voice crackled from our small radio, and after the official news was read, a less formal sporting commentary ensued:

> "Now onto the exciting bit of news about the car rally which started gloriously this morning in Dar es Salaam, the beautiful port by the sea. All cars have completed their run up to Dodoma in good time, except for an unfortunate accident. More on that shortly. But first, in the lead are the Scandinavians in their Saab coupe number 25, second to reach Dodoma were Burt Shakeland and Jonathan George, number 15 in their Peugeot 404, and third were Kenyans Pravin Metha and Curt Flaming in their new Datsun sport coupe, number 5.
>
> "Unfortunately, Joginder Singh and Stanley Cooper met with an accident along the way as their car skidded off the muddy road and hit a large tree. They escaped injuries but the car seems to be out of action, so they have dropped out of the race.
>
> "And finally, the only Tanzanian first-time entrants, Zully Remtullah and Nizar Panjwani in Saab No 6, the African Zebra, have surprised everyone. They came into Dodoma in 10th place ahead of legendary Italians Reno Marino and Carlo Amoretti. If the African Zebra continues with its pace, who knows what awaits at the end of the first leg.
>
> "Whether the newcomers' performance so far is merely fluke or sheer skill remains to be seen, for it is a long, grueling way to the finish line. Endurance

*and experience, at the end of the day, will prevail over
fortune.*

*"In other sports news, the African Cup qualifying
rounds…"*

We all jumped, elated! Paku, as usual, dashed out,
grazing the door, losing balance and stumbling over the
stairs onto the courtyard. As usual, he got up as fast as he
went down, running with both hands in the air, screaming
"Sardaji is out, Joginder is out!"

The following day, the newspapers had detailed accounts
of Joginder Singh's misfortune, but the headlines dominated
the good run by the African Zebra, and both were the topic
of every discussion during school recess. We couldn't wait
to get home to catch the news.

That evening we huddled, once cain, in front of the radio
as it crackled to life:

> *"Good evening everyone. The final stretch of the first leg
> from Dodoma to Kampala was not uneventful. Ten cars
> were disqualified as they broke down. Our reporters from
> the villages nearby say the roads this year are treacherous
> because of extra rains, which left deep potholes. When
> hit at over 120 mph, the impact to the underside of the
> car is damaging. Most cars lost or completely broke their
> axles, and repairing would take too long. The lucky ones
> just escaped or spotted the potholes just in time to avoid
> the inevitable plunge to death.*
>
> *"Time is of the essence here because the drivers
> would want to gain as much in this leg as they can to
> give them leverage for the second leg.*
>
> *"So in the lead are still the Swedes Johansson and
> Erickson, in their trademark Saab, followed, once*

"Soon you will be attending a mixed school. Students from other Asian communities will be your classmates, Africans or Arabs, even Europeans. You have to be sensitive and respectful of others around you."

Then Amin paused for a moment, and said, "You know, we as a community have to change our attitudes. We have to accept others. If not, we will be gone, sent off, wiped with history!"

"Do you understand what I am saying?" he asked gravely, like a school master.

I nodded like a reprimanded student, not comprehending the depth of his concern. But what I grasped was that I led a sheltered life. We all did in those rows of flats, going to the same parochial school, attending the same mosques, playing with the same boys, hardly ever venturing outside or inviting someone inside.

The rest of the way home, we walked in silence, his comforting arm was around my shoulders. To our right, the vast Indian Ocean expanded to the distant horizon, where ships would vanish into the void after leaving our harbor of peace.

The following morning, Amin woke me and beckoned me to come down soon as rally cars would be rolling into Nairobi in the next couple of hours. Soon, it would be over; the anxiety mounted.

Downstairs, Mother had made English breakfast; Dad was in the sitting room, buried behind his *Standard News* paper. Amin, as usual, was absorbed in one of his borrowed novels. And Shafiq on the side seat read the sports section of the paper.

"Jamil, Jamil!"

We heard, once again, the dreaded cries from the courtyard.

Shafiq jocularly said, "Move that sofa before he comes crashing in."

I signaled him from the window, and before I opened the door, Paku was right there, in my face.

Paku moved swiftly into the living room, sat on a couch next to our audio system, and greeted my dad, "*Ya Ali,* uncle."

Dad lowered his newspaper and acknowledged him, while Amin gave him a perfunctory smile and a nod.

Paku pleaded, "*Bana*, turn it on, turn it on, weh!"

In the last twenty-four hours, much had transpired. According to the reports, only twenty-five cars remained and were heading towards their final destination: Nairobi. The rest were disqualified or retired: car trouble, late arrivals at check-points, and many had succumbed to the harsh, treacherous, and wet-muddy roads.

The final northeastern leg — the notorious Nakuru circuit — claimed many victims. But the African Zebra remained in the race, only eight cars behind the Swedish leaders.

Overwhelmed, we sat there in silence waiting anxiously for the final report.

At last, the moment we all waited for came to its end. The Swedes won, with Burt Shakeland and Jonathan George in second place, followed by Pravin Metha. The African Zebra finished sixth, matching its registration number.

The following day, the *Standard Daily News*, had screaming headlines about the Tanzanian victory, displaying pictures of victorious Burt Shakeland and the debutant performers, Remtullah and Panjwani. All accounts of how the African Zebra managed to outwit its veteran participants dominated the newspapers. The national euphoria was amplified in our neighborhood, in the streets of Dar, even among the African populace.

Caretaker

In the way that elegant minarets, manicured lawns, and lush gardens with sparkling water fountains are inherently part of a grand mosque, Mr. Karmali was a human one. He was our *jamat bhai,* or caretaker, of the Upanga Mosque at the end of several rows of two-story, cream-white, identical flats along the bending Upanga Road.

It is a modern two-story, white building with arched glass windows along the length of each floor, and a prominent tower at one end, housing four circular clocks on each of its faces and a dome on top. It looks majestic and ostentatiously conspicuous, more like a palace than a house of worship. Perhaps all houses of worship are deliberately built on a grander scale to inspire awe among its worshipers — and envy among those not of the denomination. Even in Europe, ancient cathedrals were built on enormous scale. So were the temples of ancient India, followed by Muslim conquers who built their grand mosques, some on razed temple grounds.

On festive occasions, our Upanga Mosque was festooned with glittering colored lights along the edges of the building, outlining its frame at night. Many postcards captured this luminous moment and were on sale at many of the local bookstores in town. It was a landmark of its kind and a source of architectural pride for our community, not only the Upanga Mosque, but others as well, in downtown, in Kariako, in other coastal and interior towns. These landscape monuments spoke of the community's powerful presence — and for many a source of envy.

Every morning and evening before prayers, Mr. Karmali would be seated in his rickety wooden chair by the main entrance doors. His appearance and attire, like the unchanging engraved Arabic designs on the entrance doors, remained unaltered: a white flowing *kanzu* concealing his large body, a brown tweed jacket adorned with old bronze medals with ribbons, and a tilted red fez on his oversized head, its black tassel, like a pendulum, brushed his unshaven jovial face as he greeted people entering the prayer hall.

He rarely spoke, and when he did, it was only to delegate mosque-related chores in Kiswahili to youngsters. His *Kutchi and Gujarati* were heavily accented with African pronunciations, and was often ridiculed by the affluent kids who attended Friday prayers in their best designer clothes.

In the children's presence and other adults of similar social status, he addressed them in Kiswahili, reversing the ridicule and discomfort, for these affluent *Tanzanians* (as they called themselves) spoke the national language with limited and embarrassing lack of fluency, even though they were part of second or third generation immigrants.

The island of Zanzibar was his original home, where his forefathers had emigrated from India in the early part of 1880 when the Arab and Sultan dynasty flourished along the coastal cities and islands of East Africa. The vocation of *jamat bhai,* like that of a Hindu caste, was passed down with each generation. His great grandfather served in the mosque in British India in the city of Bombay; his grandfather and father, during the Sultan dynasty, served on the islands of Pemba and Zanzibar; and now, Mr. Karmali, on the mainland, in the city of Dar es Salaam at one of the modern mosques in Upanga.

Such was Mr. Karmali's legacy of devotion and service to the imam of the community, its mosque, and its followers. He wore the relics of this dying legacy, captured in medals, on his brown jacket, as visual displays of an unwritten past. He had no progeny to bequeath the knowledge to, nobody to carry on the tradition.

One Friday evening at the end of the prayer activities — after the *mukhis* departed, leaving Mr. Karmali to close up — I slipped in through the front door, and found Mr. Karmali in the shoe stall, sitting in a chair too small for his overflowing body.

Mine were the only unclaimed shoes. He seemed upset that I held him from embarking upon his next chores.

"What are you doing here so late? Everybody is gone. These must be your shoes. Come on, *haraka*, I have to close up and clean."

He got up, the chair creaking from the burden of his weight, and guided me out the front door. His white *kanzu*, crumpled with creases awkwardly stuck around his wide waist.

"Can I help you? I asked, willfully.

He considered my offer, casting a quizzical look, full of suspicion about my motives.

Recently strangers and stragglers had walked into the mosque. Small items had gone missing. Some of the community's unorthodox prayer rituals were published in pamphlets in vivid and embarrassing details, questioning the practice of idolatry and fundraising during prayer times. The community had come under the scrutiny of other Muslim sects for our exclusivity, so the caretakers were instructed by the *mukhis* to be suspicious of unfamiliar faces.

Mr. Karmali squinted at me, focusing his gaze, and said, "You're not a volunteer, eh? I have not seen you help here before."

"No. I am not, but I live in the flats, in row one, number 7."

Mr. Karmali asked, "Whose son are you?"

I told him but it did not register. Only after revealing my maternal grandparents' birthplace in Chwaka in Zanzibar did Mr. Karmali warm up. He said his family lived near the *Darkhana* in town, but he knew of the area and the *mukhi* and the *jamat bhai* there. Chwaka was a poor part of Zanzibar, with thatched huts and mud-built houses with corrugated iron roofs. But he understood where I came from, and we established a commonality of heritage.

Such was a quintessential protocol of trust and confidence between a youngster and an adult in our community: your family's tie to the community, the mosque you attended, and your lineage.

"Okay, you can help me. Go to the kitchen and help Shabani put away the dishes. Then meet me upstairs," Mr. Karmali said softly like a mentor does to his pupil.

His mannerism had changed; it softened a bit because I had addressed him in his language, the way my grandmother taught me – minor *Swahili* inflections, subtle hand gestures, gentle and limp slap of both hands, fingertips brushing each other, and timely proverbial *tarab* sayings. It was a style of banter unique to the inhabitants of the isles; many mainlanders enviously labeled it as the *jungbari or unguja* charm.

I left Mr. Karmali by the shoe stall, darted out the side door, and walked to the kitchen area in the back.

Outside, the air was still, trapping the jasmine fragrance from the surrounding mosque gardens. Without moonlight, the parking lot was dimly lit by naked light bulbs, and beyond the mosque gates, tall, silver-coated street lamps on the road illuminated patches of its pavement in elliptical pools of light.

Shabani was a young African of medium height and slender build, probably in his early twenties, with clear white eyes and a smooth round face, a sharp nose and a thin mouth — common of coastal people. His neatly-pressed white shirt and khaki trousers gave him the look of a university student, except for his rubber sandals, which exposed his calloused heals and hardened, yellow toe nails.

"Ah, *ndugu* Shabani, how are you? Mzee Karmali sent me to help you," I extended my hand, which he firmly grabbed.

Shabani said, "Good, Good; I have washed all of it. You can dry them and put them in the cabinet, while I sweep up."

He gave me dry rags and dishes accumulated from food offerings brought to the mosque. Some were spread out on the tin-covered countertop table; others lay on the wooden table along the cabinet. I went to work.

During the course of my duty, Shabani and I talked about various things: football, school, other places he had worked, and his family. I discovered Shabani lived in Kinondoni, an African district of limestone dwellings and corrugated iron roofs north of Upanga, on the way to Oyster Bay. He usually took the last bus before midnight; occasionally, when he missed the bus, he would spend the night with the *askari* in his quarters – small, detached rooms behind the mosque once used for storage but now converted into a living space for short respite.

His other job, three times a week, was as an assistant cook for a wealthy Indian household in Oyster Bay. Occasionally, his father tended the mosque gardens and did the landscape, and because of his father's recommendation, Shabani acquired employment and came into Mr. Karmali's confidence.

"We are done. You can go home early today," I said excitedly.

He gave a hearty laugh and profusely thanked me. I wondered if he did all kitchen chores by himself, or other volunteers helped, for clearly that night, after the Friday festivities, he was alone. Yet, he did his job diligently and efficiently, multitasking between chores like a professional chef does cooking. I had never stayed so late.

We parted. I walked down the hall, up the short flight of stairs, and into the main prayer hall. The fragrance of incense still lingered. Unoccupied, it looked huge, its floor covered with reed carpet, and a lush red carpet along its center divided the hall into two quadrants. These were separate praying areas for men and women.

Along each of the four walls hung a couple of large, gilded, framed pictures of the smiling, benevolent imam, his eyes casting down onto his followers. I remember as a little boy, during prayers, when our eyes were supposed to be shut, I would peek, and notice the eyes from the picture staring at me. At private moments like this, such exposure of images from very early childhood became part of your mental landscape. And other times, I felt the picture may come to life.

Propped against the rear wall was another huge, framed picture just above an elaborate wooden structure, with engraved railings along its perimeter. It looked like a raised bed, covered in satin sheets on which fresh flowers and coins were strewn and scattered, offerings from the devotees.

Mr. Karmali was crouched by the elaborate wooden structure, or *takaht*, and from a small open door on its front panel, he stuffed money into a gunny sack.

He saw me standing by his side. He looked up, smiled, and handed me an empty, small gunny sack, and said, "Put the money in here. Then put all the flowers in the garbage."

His delegation of chores had the same monotonous tone as before, and a predictable pattern: first one task, then another.

He handed me a broom with a soft cloth to scoop up the flowers and offerings on the satin sheets.

I paid no attention to the amount (but it was a lump sum) as I raked in the cash, and stuffed the gunny sack. In a paper bag, I swiped in all the jasmine flowers — some fresh, others turning rusty around the unfolding petals.

"Wait for me here" he said, and then Mr. Karmali walked briskly across the hall, holding a stuffed gunny sack with cash in each hand, and he disappeared through a doorway. His heavy footsteps echoed in the quiet prayer hall. I reckoned there was a safe somewhere at the end of the hallway where Mr. Karmali vanished. Money offerings by the devotees were probably safely stashed there.

What happened to all the funds, nobody questioned, and if you did, you were told it is used for community building projects. The evidence of it, many claimed, was obviously around you: community mosques, schools, hospitals, welfare for the less fortunate, housing development.

Moments later, Mr. Karmali reappeared with his trademark medal-adorned brown coat over his flowing *kanzu* and beckoned me to follow him. We walked down the marble stairs and back to the shoe stall where we had started.

Mr. Karmali extended his hand, and gave me a broad smile. His clammy and calloused palm engulfed mine.

"Thank you. It is time for you to go home, son. Your parents will be worried," he said.

"Can I help you next Friday?"

He pondered for a moment, the squint in his eyes showed hesitation and doubt. Obviously, my intentions were honorable. I did want to help him. But I was also interested in the mystery behind his medals. Comical and clumsy they appeared — often they were objects of unmerciful mockery.

"You should sign up as a volunteer," he responded quickly.

"I am here only on vacation. I read my Advanced Levels in Iringa at the Mkwawa High School, so I don't come to the mosque often."

Mr. Karmali said, "But you do go to the mosque in Iringa, don't you?"

"Yes, but only on festive days. We have to study every day. And school is a bit far from town."

Mr. Karmali pursed his lips like a fish, moved them left to right, and said, "Okay, just help Shabani, and then meet me upstairs next Friday."

I knew the hesitation about giving me chores was because I was not a volunteer, had no rank and was not part of his daily scene of assistants. But I had spoken to a voice inside him; I had stirred some hidden emotion or reminded him of an incident from his buried past.

I bid farewell to Mr. Karmali. I walked the dirt path along Upanga Road. It is a short, brisk walk to my house, but African nights, with their darkness, seemed eternal. The street lamps dimly lit the pavement, but along the dirt road, only patches of road were traceable by small or dim, naked bulbs of the corner houses.

High hedges around corner flats provided ideal spots for a mugger to pounce on its victim. But often there were *askaris*, equipped with bows and arrows, *mrungus* or *pangas* and a whistle, walking about and guarding each row of flats. They announced their presence with flashlights, deterring the nocturnal opportunists, for we tenants were easy prey.

At night, the ocean breeze from the Indian Ocean carried its salty smell mixed with bougainvilleas and jasmine fragrance, giving the air a mild, tangy flavor.

As agreed, on the following Friday I met with Shabani in the kitchen after prayers. There was another young Asian boy in his volunteer uniform, white pressed shirt, gray slacks, and a red and green diagonally striped tie with a badge pinned to the shirt pocket. His name was Munir, and he lived in another housing development across from the mosque. He didn't stay long, didn't talk much, and stuck to one task: putting away the dishes after I dried them. Soon after the dishes and pots were washed and put away, Munir left.

Shortly after Munir left, Mr. Karmali came into the kitchen with a large plate of food — *kuku paka* and bread — and announced, happily: "Let's eat!"

He asked Shabani to bring a mat from the cupboard. He rolled it out on the floor, put the bowl in the center, and gestured us both to sit.

Shabani and I set on the mat, cross-legged. Mr. Karmali lifted his white *kanzu* over his knees, gingerly sat down, giving a large sigh of relief, praising the Lord, as though the act relieved pain from his aching joints. His large belly obstructed his cross-legged posture, and he winced from discomfort, so he sat with one leg extended, while the other slightly folded. He handed the loaf of bread to Shabani first, who cut a small portion and passed it to me.

"The *mukhi* brought this for us," he said, "My favorite, but not as good as my mother's. May her soul rest in peace," he added, looking up to the heavens.

We all ate from the same large bowl of thick, coconut yellow curry, rich and spicy, dipping our bread in turns, scooping generous portions of shredded chicken and its thick, yellow, oily sauce, relishing every bite.

Shabani said, "Too much coconut. Not cooked well."

Mr. Karmali laughed and mockingly said, "You cook next time, eh?"

During the course of the meal, Mr. Karmali told us that his mother had died of a long illness. There was no reference to his father. In our community, youngsters showed too much deference to elders. They only spoke when spoken to; asking a direct question was considered rude, so I did not probe. My father always encouraged us to challenge, to ask questions, to probe. I waited for the right moment; and let a moment of weakness with Mr. Karmali take its natural course. And so with Mr. Karmali, I had to wait for the opportune time to unravel the mystery behind his metallic decorations. People always have a history; some bury it out of shame; others wear it; and rarely does anyone in our part of the world record it.

"Don't finish everything. Leave something for my cat. She loves *kuku-paka*," Mr. Karmali said jovially.

Shabani and I chuckled, but he meant it. He asked me to get a small bowl from the cabinet in which he poured the leftovers.

On his way upstairs, through the hallway lined with shut glass windows, Mr. Karmali let out a thunderous fart and praised the Lord again. During the meal, he burped, praising the Lord each time.

Shabani and I went to work. I knew my rendezvous point with Mr. Karmali after, so we began our tasks diligently, bantering while sweeping and mopping the floor. Shabani, like the week before, was happy to go home early.

Shabani confided in me that he wanted to become a chef, an Indian chef, and some day in the future, own an Indian restaurant, which would cater mainly to African patrons in his district. Africans, he said, loved and savored Indian cuisine.

That was a novel entrepreneurial idea, but I wondered where he would acquire the capital to finance such venture -— not from his father who tended to mosque gardens part time; not from Shabani's salary, which I imagined, was a minimum pay. He told me he had spoken to Mr. Karmali about his venture, and Mr. Karmali was supportive. Mr. Karmali said he would speak to the *mukhi*, who had connections in the community.

After Shabani departed, I proceeded upstairs in the main prayer hall to whatever awaited me.

The *takaht* was devoid of its offerings, cleared by Mr. Karmali, and the money stashed away in its covert safe. I reckoned he had other chores for me tonight, but there was no sign of Mr. Karmali in the prayer hall.

Light poured into the men's side of the prayer hall from the open doorway at the end of men's section, near the water drinking area.

Walking towards the doorway, I called out for Mr. Karmali. My voice echoed in the empty hall, its acoustics amplified it. Prayer halls reverberate sound, and skilled preachers and orators capitalize that.

"Over here," replied Mr. Karmali, "in the balcony."

Across from the water counter area, a narrow walkway along the terrazzo floor lead to small jutted balcony.

Mr. Karmali was seated in the chair, his large body flowing from it. He gestured me to sit on the empty chair next to him.

"I come here and drink my *kava* before I close up and go home," Mr. Karmali declared, pouring some for me in a miniature cup from a cone-shaped bronze container.

From the balcony, the manicured mosque lawns appeared flat like a shiny, fibrous, green carpet. And when the night clouds flowed across the face of the full, luminous moon, the lawn lost its glistening appearance. The air was still and damp on this balmy December night. The incessant chirping of crickets muffled a dog's bark in the distance.

Beyond the mosque perimeter, other houses and modern tenements appeared grand compared to our monotonous rows of two-storied white flats. I didn't know anyone who lived there. They were faceless to us just as we were to them. We were a fractious lot; Asian people of other religions or Muslim sects lived there, but I knew what they thought of us and of the grand mosque: restrictive and off limits during festive days, its celebrations grand and boisterous, often ostentatiously public yet inaccessible to them.

"Look at that house at the end. That is mine!" Mr. Karmali pointed to the first house in the last row.

It was a nondescript house like all others in that row. Mr. Karmali was not wearing his fez hat, but had his brown jacket with the medals on. His hair was thinning from the front with salt-and-peppered hair around the sides, matching the specks of white in his moustache and sideburns. His round face glistened from sweat under the moonlight.

"Your cat really likes *kuku-paka*?"

Mr. Karmali laughed, his belly heaving.

"Hehe..Hehe..*Kabisa*. She loves it. My mother would give her some, and she would lick the whole bowl. That *mpaka* is a funny one," Mr. Karmali said.

Then he continued, "My mother found her one day outside our house, so small, still blind from birth, crying. So she took her in, and started feeding her with cloth soaked in milk. She stayed with us since then. Five years now."

Mr. Karmali was warming up to me, revealing his tender side. His voice had taken a softer tone, his facial muscles at ease, without the normal stern look he wore while behind the shoe counter, handling worshippers' shoes and sandals. I had to capitalize on this moment and ask him about the medals.

"Were you ever in the army?"

Mr. Karmali was amused by my query. He chuckled, glanced at the medals on his jacket, and then looked straight ahead.

"No. They belong to me, my father, and my grandfather," he said solemnly.

Then silence. And after a moment, I pressed on.

"Were you all in the British colonial army in Zanzibar and India? They look very impressive and honorable."

Even in the moonlit balcony, I could make out the colored ribbons, silver stars, lapel pins, and golden medals — a couple with Aga Khan III and IV monographs on them — others with unidentifiable figures. All, upon closer inspection, had a faded glory.

"No," Mr. Karmali said, still looking straight into the darkness.

"They were given to us for lifetime service to the community," Mr. Karmali said with a tone of confidence and pride.

"Can you tell me more about them?"

"It is a long story," Mr. Karmali said with a tinge of melancholy.

He smiled at me, condescendingly, as if brushing me off. Perhaps I misjudged his tender mannerism earlier. He probably wondered why this youngster would want to know about his past, his medals. No one before me had shown curiosity about his objects of affection and his buried past. Others considered them fake relics of self-importance, self-grandeur, and self-empowerment.

After time and after some cups of *kava*, Mr. Karmali talked for a couple of hours and I listened. This ritual of drinking *kava* and talking in the balcony after finishing chores continued for several days.

Just as the burning mist in the high country dissipates slowly, exposing its buried scars, Mr. Karmali's long story unraveled day after day.

In 1830, he told me, while his grandfather, Ladha Karmali, was a *jamat bhai* for a local mosque village in *Gujarat*, the imam at the time delivered sermons to his growing community (who lived in the poverty-ridden Indian province of Gujarat) to look westwards to East Africa and the spice island of Zanzibar for economic prosperity. The imam, during his visit in the province, summoned a small group of men from the village mosque one night into his private hut and solemnly said, "You are the chosen few who have served me and the community well here. Now I want you to take long journey to Zanzibar and establish our community presence over there. It is not an easy journey. It is not an easy country, but you will have all my blessings and you will always be in my thoughts and prayers."

He then reached into his tray of offerings and picked up a few silver coins and gave each this token of faith.

"This is a special medal for your bravery and sacrifice," he declared.

A month later, a dozen members of the mosque (including his grandfather) embarked from Portbander on an adventurous journey westwards across treacherous seas on a merchant *dhow* to Zanzibar. It took over eight weeks to reach the island of Zanzibar. But only nine of them survived; two died halfway from an inexplicable sickness, and one on the white-washed sands of the Zanzibar coastline.

At the time, East African coastal towns were under the rule of the Omani Arabs of Muscat, with the capital relocated to Zanzibar from Muscat. Their rulers were propped up by the British Empire to protect their interests in various wealthy East African countries that were rich in natural resources.

Trade flourished. Traders prospered. From India, Portugal, Persia, and Arabia, *dhows* traversed vast seas, importing — willingly — human cargo seeking wealth to fulfill their immigrant dreams and exporting — forcibly — African slaves uprooted to fulfill their master's dreams.

At the height of the flourishing British Empire in India and East Africa, these dozen men set sail for grander pastures, oblivious of the fact that they would be making history as pioneers of their community.

"Did they know anybody in Zanzibar?"

"Yes, there were a few traders from our community there already. Well connected with the Sultan. They received and accommodated them," said Mr. Karmali.

All, Mr. Karmali explained, was arranged by the imam to receive these newcomers, employ and assist them in their new land. In a short while, the new arrivals and the established traders of Zanzibar, with the help of the sultan's influence, acquired land and built their first mosque in 1838, and Ladha Karmali became the first *jamat bhai*.

Within a few years, many immigrants arrived from Kutch, Gujarat, and Sind, at the advice of their imam, seeking opportunities, joining their departed spouses, and reuniting with their families. As a result, the community grew and prospered, and unlike indentured workers before them brought to other parts of Africa from India, these newcomers were merchants and traders, and commerce was as natural to them as breathing air.

What was left behind by these immigrants thousands of miles in India resumed again in Zanzibar, preserved and untainted, providing them a sense of security, exclusion and protection from the alien environment.

A year after the mosque was built, Ladha Karmali took on a bride, Gulbanu Kassamji, who was distantly related to one of his early traveling companions. The married couple lived in a small stone house with a corrugated roof behind the mosque. They had six children. All but two died of mysterious diseases before the age of ten. At the time, child mortality was high; medical help was administered by elders resorting to traditional medicine; and often, it was of no avail.

As a wedding gift, Ladha Karmali was given another medal of honor for his services to the community, his bravery and courage to travel a treacherous journey to new land as one of early pioneers. The silver medallion was a coin with the imam's face engraved on it to commemorate the building of the first community mosque in Zanzibar.

It was not uncommon for sons to follow their father's vocation, so naturally, Ladha Karmali's son, Nasurddin Karmali, followed in his footsteps and became the successor to his father as the *jamat bhai* of the Zanzibar *Darkhana* mosque in 1905. By then, the community had grown considerably; many community members had ventured across the waters to Dar es Salaam on the mainland and from there, interior to small towns as far west as Lake Tanganyika and up north to Lake Victoria; the slave trade was abolished in the British colonies; a new sultan, under British protectorate, ruled Zanzibar briefly until 1963 when the island received its constitutional independence.

All that time, the commerce, clove, and spice trade flourished along the coast. The new immigrants became prosperous, as did the descendants of the ruling Omani Arabs. Evidently, Zanzibar developed from its lucrative trade; its propped-up ruling class of descendants of Omani Arabs and the new immigrants lived in the affluent areas of Zanzibar, turning a deaf ear and a blind eye to the winds of political change and the clock of history around them.

Whilst Ladha Karmali and family stayed, over the years, in their stone house with a corrugated roof behind the mosque, close to the town market, surrounded by narrow streets with merchant shops and houses with iconic and engraved wooden doors, they learned the local customs and language, and adopted the gracious ways of their new home. Their neighborhood was of mixed races: Africans, Arab-Africans, Hindus, and other Asian Muslims of a different sect from theirs.

Prosperity never reached the native Africans, and the indigenous African population remained impoverished and isolated. Over the years, buried rage from the brutal and inhuman slavery days festered towards the ruling class and the new immigrants: Asians. Though by the 1960s, the majority of them were born and raised on the island. It was matter of time before a demagogue would emerge and stoke the burning rage of the silent and discontented mob, culminating in a volcanic explosion of cathartic and revolutionary massacre. Such a person manifested as John Okello, who led a small army of revolutionaries and toppled the Sultan dynasty that had ruled for a century one early morning of January, 1964.

What followed after the revolution for the next couple of days was indiscriminate massacre, pillaging, and the raping of Arab and Indian women. In their path to the center of town, the mob dragged their victims out of their stone houses, killed the men, raped the women, and then clubbed or hacked them with *pangas*. That fateful morning, Ladha Karmali was on his way to the mosque when he heard of killings in the nearby district. He got the word that the mob was on the way towards the center of town, pillaging and looting along the way.

Ladha Karmali quickly gathered all the members — young children, men and women, older people — of the surrounding town and ushered them into the community mosque, and locked the massive gates and doors to its main entrance, which were formidable to break down. The mosque became the fortress against the invading and raging mob. But in all that confusion, Ladha Karmali forgot his own daughter, Reshma, who was spending the night with an uncle in the nearby district, close to where the mob was. Some men of the mosque and Ladha Karmali set foot to rescue them; they never came back.

The next day — after the sultan and his entourage fled the island, and calm was restored with the help of the former colonials and the army from the mainland — Mr. Karmali and four men left the confines of the mosque in search of his father and sister and the small band of men who left the previous night.

Along the dirt road to the district, lined with arching coconut trees close to the pristine coastline of emerald blue waters from which intermittent salty breeze pursued Mr. Karmali and the men, signs of carnage were everywhere: maimed bodies of African and Arabs lay on the road, their dry blood mixed with red soil. Among a small heap of fly-infested bodies piled up like discarded coconut husks, Mr. Karmali found his sister and father — their bodies decapitated along with other men from the mosque.

In town on the narrow pathways with arching doors to small houses on each side, they saw blood smeared on the doors; pregnant Arab, mixed-raced, and Indian women lay dead, their faces contorted from pain, their bellies ripped apart, their fetuses and intestines disemboweled; others still clutched to their doorways, their nails leaving scars of restraint on the wooden doors. The smell of death was everywhere around them.

Such horror befell Mr. Karmali as a young man — only fifteen then — and all this time, he never told anyone. His mother never recovered; its pain gradually killed her like a slow cancer. The imam of the time posthumously awarded Ladha Karmali with several medals of bravery and sacrifice. He had acted courageously and saved many lives, the imam said to his mother.

These metallic relics of history adorned on Mr. Karmali's brown coat lapel carried the weight, the burden and the pain of history, never chronicled, only forgotten and buried with death of each generation, until now. He told me they were his balm for the aching heart, and wearing them close to it eased the pain.

This is the story Mr. Karmali told me over several days.

A week later, after bidding a rueful farewell to Mr. Karmali and Shabani, I returned back to Iringa for my last term of the 6th form; soon upon writing my final exams, I was assigned to a year and half national service conscription camp in Mbeya, south of Iringa where I studied.

Near the end of my national service, one late afternoon, a parcel arrived for me. The camp commander brought it to my tent. It was small box addressed to me, and the sender was Shabani. I opened the box and recognized the contents, and like a revealing flash, I knew what had happened. The letter was written in Kiswahili by Shabani and addressed to me. Mr. Karmali had bequeathed the medals to me after his death.

Ndugu Amin:

I hope all is well with you. I am writing to inform you, regrettably, that Ndugu Karmali passed away a couple of weeks ago from diabetic complications. He instructed me to send you his medals, and said you know more about them than anybody else, and said he wanted you to keep them.

Ndugu Karmali kept his promise of setting me up with an Asian businessman to finance my small restaurant. I am now in partnership with Ndugu Ismail Kassam and have opened up a small restaurant in Kinondoni called Kinondoni Café on Kimati Street.

I am the chief chef and do all the cooking, while my sister, Amina, helps me at the till and with the accounts. When you visit Dar again, please visit me at the restaurant. I will cook some kuku-paka and roti, and we will all eat in remembrance of Ndugu Karmali.

*Restaurant business is good, but it is hard work,
and now I know, understand and appreciate that you
are in control of your work. What you put into it is
what you get out of it. All said, it is very fulfilling and
satisfying. I hope to see you soon.*

Kwaheri,

Shabani Ahmed.

The following year, I started my first year at the University of Dar es Salaam — or "the Hill" as we called it — studying economics and literature, and from time to time, on the way to the Hill from a weekend in town, I visited Shabani at his restaurant in Kinondoni.

Shabani seemed content and brimmed with confidence and worked efficiently running the operation. The café, one of its kind, in the district became popular, and Shabani prospered. After couple of years, Shabani opened another café close to the "Hill," which Amina ran with the help of their aging father.

In my final year at the Hill, I began to write this story as I was inspired to narrate a small piece of history behind the crusty medals. For me, it was a new beginning into my misty past — a historical void — and an incipient literary and self-discovery voyage.

The Middlemen

The daily morning racket — the clatter of the dishes and the clicks of silverware in the kitchen and the prickly crowing of the African raven — was Walji's early morning wake up call ever since he and his ailing mother moved from the hinterland into a welfare housing complex five years ago. The complex was supported by a charity organization for the less fortunate members of their lot, a common practice in his close-knit community, with donations from its prosperous and enterprising adherents.

Other families of similar fate — destitute widowers, paupers, and the downtrodden — shared the complex of smallish, two-bedroom flats, with a grimy courtyard with unkempt banana and raspberry trees in the center and a cemented perimeter wall along the length of the narrow pavement, perpendicular to Zanaki Street, in downtown Dar.

Outside the complex, to the left, the narrowly-paved street, with chipped asphalt, led to the majestic two-story mosque on Darkhana Road; to the right, on either side, a row of small, dimly-lit Indian shops lined the street, displaying newly-arrived merchandise through barred windows: toys, electronics, clothing, shoes, jewelry, house furniture, carpets, and rugs; and at the end of the street was a famous Indian jewelry store: Kanti Patel Jewelries.

Across from the housing compound during early morning hours, cars parked awkwardly along the dusty pavement as their drivers rushed quickly to the Flamingo Restaurant for quick tea and Indian snacks — *samosas* and *kebabs* — before the drivers headed to their respective business routines.

And above the restaurant was a guest house with twenty rooms, managed and owned by the restaurant owner, Mr. Lakhani, an astute businessman. The guest house furnished lodging for Indian traders from inland while on business trips — many made long trips from the interior, shopping for new merchandise for their shops, and often at night, they furtively relished in the carnal pleasures of the African city's nocturnal activities.

Together, the restaurant and guesthouse offered its patrons a wealth of enterprising opportunities and access to the world beyond the shores of the Indian Ocean. And beneath the serene ambiance of music and delicious delicacies that it offered to decent families, a lucrative subterranean black market of wheeling-and-dealing flourished at its heart under the condoning eyes of Mr. Lakhani.

It was set to become Alnoor Walji's new beguiling and engulfing world.

Four years ago, after Walji finished his 5th form, he approached Mr. Lakhani one morning and assertively asked, "Mr. Lakhani, I finish school Friday. I would like to work here, learn about restaurant management and assist you with any errands."

Mr. Lakhani studied the good-looking young man with long hair parted in the middle. Walji and his mom frequented the restaurant. Often, Mr. Lakhani would decline their payment, saying, "No problem. Do not worry, Ma," and Mrs. Walji would respond in kind: "May the Lord bless you."

These acts of charity had scarred Walji in his formative years, but he helplessly endured it, and he had avowed that one day, at any cost, he would wash it off, like scum covering his body.

"Don't you want to study further? Finish your sixth form?" asked Mr. Lakhani.

"No. I am interested in the hotel management business. No book learning can substitute for real experience. You will find me very hard-working and reliable and trustworthy. I know this place gets busy. I can work the morning shift or night shift, whichever suits you. But I do want to learn the business," asserted Walji eagerly.

Such enthusiasm, thought Mr. Lakhani, was rare among young men of today. It reminded him of his early years when he slogged at his father's shop in the interior. He had no sons of his own to assist him and his two daughters were married off and lived with their husbands in the interior. He could surely use some assistance behind the counter, he thought, especially during the rush hours of morning and lunch.

"Okay, Walji, you can start next week as my apprentice," said Mr. Lakhani.

They mutually agreed on his starting salary and overtime; it was comparable to others his age with no experience. Walji would start working the morning shift, and every other Saturday — if he desired — he could work overtime. As well as handling patron bills, he would also manage the guesthouse bills. Overtime, he would handle inventory, banking, and general management issues in absence of Mr. Lakhani.

And so Walji entered his new world four years ago, with immense vigor and enterprising ambition, and Mr. Lakhani never regretted his decision. Within two years, Walji, young as he was, became the assistant manager.

Only a year into his new job, Walji suggested to Mr. Lakhani to alter the restaurant ambiance and décor — terrazzo floors in the inside, flickering neon lights shaped as prancing flamingo birds outside, a variety of music catering to all generations and races — African, Indian, Arab and European.

It all paid off; the restaurant buzzed with activity day and night with patrons: government officials, businessmen, youngsters, and travelers.

When Walji and his mother first moved into the welfare complex from the hinterland five years ago, he befriended a youngster his age, Shafiq Virani, an African adopted by Indian parents from Dodoma. They lived in the flat across the littered and bird dropping-blemished courtyard.

Both youngsters attended the same parochial secondary school where they completed their fourth form with passing grades. They continued with their fifth form but soon dropped out. Neither had any academic aspirations for further studies, but both shared the obsession with money, and they possessed the street-smarts, charm, and self-confidence as well as good looks: a perfect mixture for a team of enterprising and wily grifters in the making. Early on, both had declared to each other to make money — at any cost, by any means — to wash off the stigma of welfare dependency, which they had endured as taunts in the mosques, at school, or at social events, from the well-to-do children of other families within their community.

Amongst friends, Shafiq Virani was known as "Shaft" because of his uncanny resemblance to the black American actor Richard Roundtree, who played the character "Shaft" in a crime action-packed series, where the black American actor fought the injustice and corruption of white men in America. The cinema halls showing such films with actors like Jim Brown, Sidney Poitier, Isaac Hayes, and Richard Roundtree were packed by Asians and Africans alike.

Shafiq donned an Afro and sported a moustache to complete the image. It suited him; women, African and Asian, adored his groovy look, and he capitalized on that image.

Soon after dropping out of 5th form, like Walji, Shaft took some petty odd clerical jobs for three years — mainly working for Asian merchants doing procurement and courier runs for their banking — and later enrolled in a vocational correspondence course in office administration. After completing the course with passing grades, he landed a job as a petty clerk at a government passport processing unit, part of the Department of Customs and Immigration, filing and handling passport and visa applications, dealing with inquiries — a dreadfully boring job, with no prospects for career development. Nonetheless, he was well-placed to exploit his influence to expedite applicant's travel documents and visas, which through normal channels of bureaucracy was interminably long.

But for a small fee — *baksheesh,* money for tea or *chai,* in local parlance, a bribery — "miracles can happen if my superiors are made happy," Shaft would suggest to his applicants, and the desperate ones would oblige.

Walji approached Shaft one day and proposed a business plan: to supply Shaft with a steady clientele — travelers from the interior living at the guest house — needing his services. And there was no shortage of people in desperate need of traveling documents quickly.

The political and economic mood had shifted in the country. It had gone the route of socialism where the *Mwalimu* and his ruling party had put the *Arusha Declaration* into practice. Asian and foreign-owned, small-scale industries, businesses, and properties were nationalized by the government. Panic and insecurity engulfed the Asian community like an impending and menacing storm of doom, and a growing sense of flight naturally infused among those with the means.

These wealthy, panic-stricken Asians — youngsters leaving for education abroad, families and professionals, from the interior and Dar, receiving their emigrant visas from Canada, England, or Australia, adults wanting to flee with allowable possessions — became Shaft's source of underground income, which he shared with Walji and other middlemen in the passport office.

One Saturday around noon, Shaft walked briskly from the welfare housing — with a small package wrapped in brown paper bag in his hand — across the street to the Flamingo restaurant. Mr. Lakhani was not there, but Walji was behind the counter, administering orders to the waiters and attending to patron's bills.

The thick aroma of fried onions and Indian species wafted from the rectangular kitchen sliding window and lingered in the dining area. A half-dozen formica tables stood at the ready, with African and Indian patrons who relished their lunch with curries of the day. Melancholic Hindi tunes of love and betrayal from the latest hit movies spewed from the hanging speakers at each corner of the eating-area walls, just above the large standing fans with grimy rotating grill keeping the area cool.

"Shafty, man, how are you?" beamed Walji from behind the glass counter, giving him the black power handshake.

"Fit *Kabisa*, man," replied Shaft.

"Listen, sit down, bana, we should talk for few minutes," said Walji with a conspiring smile, suggesting the possibility of a new, lucrative venture.

Shaft ordered his usual Saturday afternoon lunch — fish curry, rice, bread, and freshly squeezed mango juice — for which he never paid. After the lunch crowd subsided, Walji approached Shaft and set across the table.

"How did it go last week?" asked Walji.

Shaft gave him the smirk he imitated from the movie character and said, "Cool. Cool, man."

"They all in here, two hundred of them," said Shaft, placing the brown package on the table and sliding it towards Walji, who picked up the package swiftly and placed it on the empty chair next to him. He then placed a small, bulky sealed envelope, full of 100 Shilling notes, and slid it across the table to Shaft, who accepted the package and knew what to do with it.

"How is *ndugu* Kibala? Happy?" inquired Walji.

"Oh, he is going to be very pleased with this bunch. More the better," said Shaft.

Mr. Kibala was Shaft's internal African top man at the passport office who authorized all the passports and visas, and got a sizeable share of the *baksheesh* for each passport.

Shaft told Walji — jokingly — that Mr. Kibala was worried that if all Asians left, he would not have a side income from passports.

Walji smiled and said, "Next week, we are getting another bulk applications from the interior. A big one this time, so we have to be discreet. Tell that to Mr. Kibala."

"No problem, man," replied Shaft.

"Is that what you wanted to talk about?" asked Shaft, curious about Walji's somber demeanor.

"No. We have an opportunity to diversify. Possibly get big money," declared Walji.

"Okay. What? How?" asked Shaft.

Walji smiled, brushing backwards his silky long hair parted in the middle with his fingers and said: "Currency trading."

"Dollars?" asked Shaft.

"Dollars and sterling pounds, man. You see, people leaving the country have tons of shillings hoarded. Well, you know how we are. We save, save, save, put some in the bank, the rest, we stash it under the mattress and suitcase, and we hide it for rainy days. The ones for whom we are issuing passports, we can propose to assist them in converting their savings into foreign currency. Even act as middlemen to transfer it to banks outside the country. Of course, we keep a good commission. It is a risky and nasty business.

"But first we must cultivate contacts at the airports and seaports," Walji continued, "We have businessmen come here every day from the interior staying at the guest house. Some have made discreet inquiries with me if I know of anyone dealing with this sort of business.

"You are placed well at the immigration department to cultivate some contacts at the customs. I can manage deals with our potential clients here. The good thing is that they know they can trust us, because we have worked with them — getting their passports. We will have gained their confidence. And we are just extending our service in case they need to trade currency."

Walji smiled smugly, and said, "Well, Shafty, what do you think? We can make it big. This is lucrative business. It can lead to other grander ventures as well — gemstones, man!"

Shaft knew Walji was never satisfied with the passport venture. It was petty and small scale and unglamorous. He was hungry; he wanted more.

The funds from the passport commissions paid for their exuberant social lifestyle (partying with women escorts at the Africana night club on weekends, occasionally entertaining Mr. Kibala and his entourage) and familial duties (keeping their parents satisfied with groceries and tickets to Hindi movies on Sundays). It made Walji's mom proud, and Shaft's parents happy not to ask for welfare donations — now each parent had their son, like a good Indian son, providing for them.

"We should do it," said Shaft, and then added, "But there is one problem."

"What?"

"Who is going to be the courier? Bring someone in and we have to split the cut with him. It has to be either me or you?"

"I cannot be away from Mom. She needs me here all the time; she's ill. Plus Mr. Lakhani has entrusted me with this job. I practically run the entire operation for him. The guest house, the restaurant, the whole bit," Walji explained.

So the onus rested squarely on Shaft's shoulders: he would cultivate the appropriate contacts at the required ports of exit and smuggle the money out of the country. For all the risks involved, he demanded bigger share of the commission. Walji agreed to a 60/40 split. It was only fair for Shaft given the risks involved.

Shaft was confident he could do it. He was adventurous and audacious, the risk taker and he derived excitement from the unexpected. His racial duality – African and Indian – was an immense asset: Africans and Indians accepted him as one of them. He effortlessly moved between the two worlds, and he exploited it, knowing when, where and how, to his advantage (there was the cultural familiarity of the language and mannerisms of the two worlds).

The Saturday afternoon brightness poured in the eating area of the Flamingo restaurant through the wide open doors and large glass windows facing the streets. The clicks of the bicycle rings, the honks from the passing cars outside the busy street blended inside with Hindi tunes from the movie *Dosty* in the background, while Shaft and Walji swore to a brotherly oath: If one of them is apprehended, the other should flee the country; neither should compromise their contacts.

So an insidious venture of currency trading scheme was initiated, their next step into the deceitful and treacherous underground world. Jumping passport queues was petty; siphoning national taxable income illegally out of the country was an ultimate act of treason.

Walji agreed to foster the clientele, mainly the visiting businessmen from the interior staying at the guest house. At first, he suggested, he would target those who requested passport services, and then perhaps woo local rich Asian tycoons, after a few successful runs and after all the logistics are sorted out.

Both were thrilled with what lay ahead: the possibility of amassing large commissions and relishing a lavish life style denied them by their downtrodden upbringing and charity dependency.

"Well, we should celebrate tonight at the club," Shaft suggested.

"*Kabisa*, man," replied Walji.

They parted, only to meet later in the evening for celebratory drinks.

On the following Monday, Shaft was anxious to return to work and peruse his office directory in search of a facilitator, an official in the customs department, someone not too highly ranked (a high-ranking official would demand a large cut, shrinking the commission pie he thought), but someone with jurisdiction over the airport customs so that on the day of departure, the custom official on duty at the airport checkpoint would be instructed to wave Shaft through, without searching his luggage. He thought of one person who had trained him early on but now had moved on to the customs department.

The Department of Customs and Immigration had moved from fusty offices with corrugated roofs near the harbor into a lavish and modern seven story-tall concrete building, with large rectangular glass windows on each floor, on Ghana Road, halfway between city center and the residential area of Upanga, across from the vast and leafy Gymkhana golf course and cricket ground.

The customs department was located on the fourth floor of the office building, and the immigration department, where Shaft worked, was on the first floor. The top three floors were leased to foreign companies, mainly British, some Scandinavian.

When Shaft first joined the immigration department a couple of years ago, he shared an office with a junior officer named Joseph, an African slightly older than him, reserved, respectful, and diligent. Joseph sometimes handled custom claims for those goods confiscated by officials at ports of entry and later claimed by rightful owners as legitimate possessions. For Shaft's initial months at work, Joseph trained him in clerical duties for passport and visa application processing. Shaft was his apprentice.

Joseph enjoyed Shaft's gregarious personality and envied his popularity with women at work and the young European female travelers, who came in for visa extensions. These lady travelers always asked for Shaft, as if their friends from their respective countries had recommended Shaft to them. Joseph lacked the social grace with the opposite sex, and was conscious of it (once he had confided in Shaft his timidity with women).

A year later, Joseph was promoted to senior officer and transferred to the customs department. After the transfer, Shaft saw less of Joseph, only sometimes in the canteen in the company of other senior officers, dressed in smart customs uniform — starched, white shirt, with shoulder lapels, and dark trousers. And when their eyes met, Joseph would acknowledge him with a polite nod.

That Monday October morning, after completing the mundane clerical duties — filing applications, picking up the approved passports from Mr. Kibala, handing out applications at the counter — Shaft slipped out and took the elevator to the fourth floor in search of Joseph.

The elevator door opened up to a small lobby where a passive and bored looking African woman, dressed in resplendent matching blouse and skirt, sat behind a counter, typing.

From the lobby, on both sides, Shaft could see narrow corridors with office doors, some shut, and others widely open, extending to the end; from the open office doors, soft incomprehensible chatter flowed into the lobby. At the end of each corridor, against the wall, was a small window through which afternoon brightness poured in and reflected on shiny floors, illuminating the passage way.

The area seemed stuffy and uninviting. It lacked the bustle of people and openness of the first floor working area: desks littered with office papers and shared by clerks; visitors flowing in and out of the area through wide glass swinging doors; applicants lined up in queues; people just milling about, waiting for their number to be called for an appointment for this or that immigration matter.

Shaft approached the African woman sitting and typing slowly behind a small office desk.

"Yes, can I help you?" she said without looking up.

"Ah. Where is Mr. Joseph Mwinyi's office?"

"Do you have an appointment?" she said, still typing away, without looking up, thinking of Shaft as just another applicant claiming their confiscated goods.

"I don't need an appointment. I work downstairs in immigration," said Shaft authoritatively with a tone suggesting the nature of the visit was business.

The receptionist looked up, and saw Shaft holding his badge, and became animated and said, "Down the corridor. Room 405. But he is out on Monday and Wednesday working at the airport."

Shaft was delighted to hear that, just what he had hoped for all weekend long, seeking a candidate as a facilitator with some influence at the airport. Joseph was that man, he reckoned.

"I will come back tomorrow," Shaft said and took the elevator back to the first floor.

The next day, Shaft returned just before lunch time. The African receptionist was absent from her desk. He walked past a few open office doors where customs officers were seating behind their desks, reading memos, signing papers or scribbling notes, and some talking on the phones, or chatting with visitors seated across on upright wooden chairs.

The offices with large glass windows and titled-named plates on the doors belonged to high-ranking officers: senior managers and supervisors. Joseph's office was at the end of the corridor. The door was closed; Shaft knocked twice.

"Come in," said Joseph softly from behind the closed door.

He was seated behind a neatly organized desk, in an upright chair, wearing his uniform, looking stern and purposeful. He looked up at Shaft, and the face of rectitude gave way to smiles.

The office was small, and the tiny glass window from which brightness flowed in was shut, trapping still hot air inside mixed with remnants of human odor from previous visitors. On the side wall, above a black file cabinet, hung two mid-sized framed pictures of the president, *Mwalimu,* and the vice-president. Every business shop, government outfit, and school displayed these familiar, benevolent, fatherly figures.

"*Karibu, Karibu,* Shafiq," said Joseph gesturing him to take a seat.

Joseph addressed him by his first name, never by Shaft, though he knew that others called him Shaft. Shaft's cultural duality always confounded Joseph. He could not quite read Shaft. He was always wary of Shaft's intentions, especially his Asian side.

When Shaft worked under Joseph, he once asked Shaft: "Who are you? What do you consider yourself?"

Shaft replied, "I am both. To people like you, I am African. To them, I am Asian. I am of two cultural worlds."

Joseph sighed and said, "I guess I will never understand your other world. It is too remote and closed for me. It is too alien."

Joseph wondered what the purpose of the visit was today after all these lapsed months. He reckoned it may be work related.

"What can I do for you?" Joseph asked, assuming the superior and official role.

"Nothing official, but something social," said Shaft, breaking into his charming laughter.

"I am throwing a small party at the Africana Hotel this Saturday. I wanted to invite you to be my special guest. I never had the chance to officially thank you, so I thought this would be a good opportunity," said Shaft, craftily selecting the words, adjusting his inflection, to emphasize Joseph's importance.

"You know lots of booze, good music, and gorgeous women. Just some fun," Shaft added, smiling.

After a silence, Joseph agreed but was unsure how to get to Africana Hotel, a beach resort on the outskirts of town, on that Saturday night. But Shaft had already sorted it out. He laid a small sealed envelope on the table and told Joseph that it should cover the taxi fare and the entrance charges. He told him he wished not to inconvenience his guests.

Was it a payment of sort?

They agreed to meet at the club bar around 9:30 pm.

On his way out, Shaft thought he ought to be congratulated. He felt victorious for setting the stage, just as he had before with Mr. Kibala — the invite and the envelope. Now Walji and Shaft had to facilitate the other bit — furnish women and booze and monies (which were flowing in steadily from passport commissions). And finally, oblige and exploit Joseph's jurisdiction at the Dar airport.

Shaft rang Walji from his desk and told him of Joseph. He said we have to do for Joseph what they did for Mr. Kibala this Saturday. But this time around, Shaft suggested, they employ Miriam's services for Joseph.

Miriam was a high-class prostitute, in her mid thirties, full and voluptuous in the Arabian sense, who had befriended Shaft. She was of mixed blood, Arab and African and Indian, and had made her way to Dar from Mombassa with a European escort who had abandoned her after promising marriage — and subsequent emigration to Denmark.

Shaft had helped her secure a working permit. Now she worked as a travel agent issuing airline tickets for an agency owned by a Sikh in town; her nocturnal activities were secret and privileged: giving pleasure to rich men, providing escort to parties, where she met many of her affluent clientele.

Sometimes, on Saturdays, she visited with Walji and Shaft at the Flamingo Restaurant for an afternoon curry, drawing lewd and envious Asian men's desirable glances, secretly coveting her.

The rest of the working Monday was uneventful for Shaft. He thought he should ring Miriam; perhaps ask her out for drinks and a meal at the New Africa Hotel. After three attempts, he finally got through to her office. Miriam said she had an engagement this evening, and Shaft knew what she meant.

Shaft asked of her company for Saturday evening. He said he was going to be with an important colleague and explained her role for the evening: entertaining his friend Joseph, in her best way, no less. Shaft told her she would be compensated adequately. A time was arranged to pick her up from her dwelling in Kariako, behind Tandamuti Street.

Shaft felt accomplished, like a puppet master, pulling all the correct strings after a successful show. He reckoned, correctly, that Joseph had a soft spot for women, especially women other than pure African; it was an obsession for him – and Miriam would fulfill that fantasy.

He imagined a series of predictable events. After their first night together, Shaft thought, Joseph would desire Miriam time and again, but Miriam would be inaccessible, costly, for Miriam would require more than what Joseph's meager civil service salary allows. Shaft would provide the supplementary income in exchange for Joseph's services rendered; with the extra money, Joseph would continue relishing in the carnal pleasures of entertaining Miriam — and others who may follow.

Shaft was confident all what he had imagined would come together, just as it had for Mr. Kibala. Human frailties and repressed desires once revealed in confidence become weapons of control for unscrupulous people like Shaft and Walji; they employ it to tug and pull, making its victims targets of manipulation.

Shaft left for the day, with an envelope of passports Mr. Kibala had given him in the morning. He felt satisfied for what he had set out to accomplish for the day.

He walked the length of Ghana Road towards the end, where it met Samora Avenue. He then crossed by the Empress Cinema, and went around the corner to the New Africa Hotel, a place favored by expatriates for evening beer after work on the outside patio facing the main street overlooking the harbor to the left.

Often after work, Walji and Shaft would meet here for drinks, sometimes in the company of Mr. Kibala and his female companions, sometimes in the company of affluent expatriates with whom they had forged friendships. Walji had thought of it before; these foreigners would come to play a pivotal role in supplying foreign currency on the black market.

On a Saturday morning, Walji walked across the street from his flat to the Flamingo Restaurant to meet with a prospect from the interior staying at the guest house. During the week, he had arranged a rendezvous. It was Walji's day off; Mr. Lakhani was attending to the business.

Walji spotted the man from the interior at the corner table reading the *Daily Standard* newspaper. He approached him, exchanged pleasantries and they both ordered Indian snacks and tea — Walji's treat.

Midweek, the man had approached Walji after lunch rush hour and introduced himself as Govind Sharma, a close associate of another middleman that Walji dealt with for passports. Between them, an unspoken understanding of the nature of business was mutually understood, like two clandestine operatives exchanging secret coded greetings; now it was time to talk about terms of engagement.

Mr. Sharma looked older than his mid-forties; he was short and stocky with a sizeable beer belly and a receding hair line. He had discolored teeth and a ruby tongue from eating the beetle juice plant leaves, *Indian pan*, which always bulged from one side of his cheeks, making his speech hardly audible.

"Ah Walji, *bhai*," he faintly said.

Walji felt a bit odd being addressed in this brotherly Indian fashion.

"When I first met you last week, I had imagined you much older. Aren't you a bit young for this business?" Mr. Sharma inquired patronizingly, as if having second thoughts about discussing his proposal with a prospective business partner much junior to him.

Mr. Sharma spitted a red ball of masticated beetle juice pulp into an empty saucer, making a reddish pulpy splatter. He then wiped the remaining crimson drip of spit suspending from his bottom lip with the napkin.

Walji thought of saying: *Where do you think you are? In your little bush house in the interior? This is a restaurant!*

But he masked his disgust with a sardonic smile and said, "Yes, but reliable. And I have good connections."

"True. True," said Mr. Sharma, who knew of Walji's reliable passports deals from their mutual friend.

"See, I have some business friends up country. Lots of money, shillings. They want to convert it to dollars or sterling pounds. Can you help?"

"Yes."

"Your rate?" asked Mr. Sharma, taking a sip of tea from his cup, and giving a sigh of relief.

Walji told him.

Mr. Sharma pondered and considered it. It was reasonable, within his expectation of the current black market: 150.00 shillings for a US dollar and 290.00 shillings for sterling pound. Plus, he thought, there was the reliability and comfort factor: Walji was a known entity.

Walji suggested that Mr. Sharma should inform his business associates that with reasonable fees, he can have the monies delivered outside the country. He was selling a safety package, using his permanence and communal background to his advantage, amidst the insipid fear of uncertainty lurking above the Asian community like a dark cloud of doom after the recent expropriation of their property and business assets, all for public and national interests, paving the road to the embraced socialist ideals.

Many wondered what would happen next. Perhaps their large sums of savings, some in the bank, some stashed away in secret corners of their dwellings would be up for grabs as well. Such cash was deemed as wrongfully obtained from the blood and sweat of the Africans.

Funneling monies abroad was a risky business, a gamble. Trust was paramount; absconded funds in these illegal transactions could never be reported to the authorities, so such dealings were purely grounded on mutual trust. Winning Mr. Sharma's confidence — Walji knew from those first words muttered by him about Walji's age — was crucial.

When Walji spoke to people — whether selling or proposing or advising — he conveyed a beguiling sense of probity. It made him sound and appear older and wiser than his age. And recently, Walji colored streaks of white into his hair to add years to his handsome, boyish face.

Mr. Sharma inquired, with concern, how the package — he resorted to coded words like "package" or "parcel" to refer to monies — was going to be delivered and by whom.

Walji was coy and did not reveal his courier — Shaft — but said with conviction that he had a reliable means of delivery. At the other end, in London, he would need a contact, supplied by the interested client, who would acknowledge the delivery was safely made by the courier. Until then, Mr. Sharma's clients would not part with Walji's fees: a percentage of the amount smuggled — the larger the amount, the bigger the risk, and the fatter the commission.

After a moment of silence and sipping of more tea and nibbling of Indian snacks, Mr. Sharma said, "Good. I will talk to my clients. I will be in town soon. But before that I will reach you, phone you from Tanga."

"We should be cautious of what we say on the phone," said Walji.

"*Bhai*, I know...We will use coded language," said Mr. Sharma, smiling.

Mr. Sharma reached inside his trouser pocket for the beetle juice leaf, *pan*, wrapped in triangular silver wrapping. He unfolded it, pinched the moist green leaf with his fingers and guided it into the side of his mouth and started chewing.

They bid farewell and agreed to contact each other in couple of weeks. Walji felt a sense of euphoria, that surge of confidence when a deal is won as desired by a crafty salesperson. He knew he had won Mr. Sharma's confidence by convincing him that his services were reliable without revealing any details or even giving any indication that he had never run "packages" before. Such game of confidence only seasoned grifters managed. But self-assuredness came naturally for Walji and Shaft.

All parties involved knew the inherent risks of the nature of the business — their clients depended only on word of mouth; they did not have anything else to go by; there was no guarantee, no recovery should something go awry. It was only the middlemen's trust for the final delivery of the "package"— nothing less or more.

Later in the day, Walji and Shaft met to discuss Mr. Sharma's meeting and catch up on the evening plans; they had to instruct Miriam, at any cost, to ensure Joseph was entertained exclusively that night, and she would be paid handsomely for all the tricks of her trade.

On weekends, outside the restaurant on the street, a fleet of taxis waited for prospective fares — diners from the restaurant and lodgers from guest house upstairs. Walji and Shaft employed the services of one particular driver,

Osman, an Arab, who gave them good fares, especially on weekends; he would be their designated driver for the rest of the evening.

That Saturday evening, Osman drove them to the Africana Hotel, picking up Miriam on the way — from her flat in the residential area of Kariako, behind the Tandamuti Street, across from the market. The district was an old settlement, mainly inhabited by Arab and Indian shopkeepers; Africans lived alongside in low cement dwellings with corrugated roofs.

Shaft and Miriam bantered during the ride; at one point, Shaft reminded her of Joseph and she smiled, disguising her irritation at the reminder. Miriam's dark, wavy hair reached her broad exposed shoulders. She wore a tightly fitted yellow dress with floral patterns that accentuated her full curvy body. Whenever the passing street lamps cast their fleeting light on her smooth and radiant face, she glowed of chocolate beauty. Her narrow eyes and the black eyeliner around her eyelids gave her the seductive appearance of an Egyptian heroine.

Walji remained disengaged; his mind explored ways to garner large amounts of foreign currency —— dollars and sterling pounds — should Mr. Sharma require a bulk sum for his clients. A sum of more than ten thousand would entail alternative means. Perhaps, he thought, he would suggest his expatriate friends deposit a sum in an account that Shaft would then have access to during his trips abroad; small amounts would be easy. Over the past six months, he had amassed close to eight thousand dollars that he had bought from his expatriate friends on the black market.

The Bagamoyo Road to the Africana Hotel ran along vast patches of open and scrub vegetation, stretching to the shores of the Indian Ocean on one side along the tarmac road. The shimmering reflection of the bright yellow moon — cutting now and then through the small puffy clouds — on the calm Indian Ocean heartened Walji when he peered out the window, and followed its motion along the ripples of water. It had a liberating effect on him, relieving his worries, absorbing his fears and anxieties as its wavy image on the water surface traveled alongside with them.

Finally, Osman turned onto a dirt road to lead them to the main entrance, about a mile inland. Shaft paid the entrance fees. After dropping his party at the main parking lot of the beach resort, Osman said he would return just before closing time — he knew the routine.

The beach resort took pride in boasting its "African wildlife" experience. It had a miniature zoo: a couple of lions in large cages often roared loudly at night, more out of boredom than anything else; a few giraffes strolled around in tall, gated fences; a few chimps swung from a large enclosed area; and some zebras and wilder beasts lazily stood, motionless, behind the monkey cages. When downwind from this beastly entrapment, the stench was offensive.

First time Europeans guests were bewildered and enchanted by the miniature wildlife scenery. It was an introduction to what lay ahead of them at the open game parks in the interior. But the regular patrons ignored it; they went straight to the open bar and cavernous dance area.

Miriam, flanked by Walji and Shaft, walked past the wildlife along the paved path to the open bar where people mingled and gathered before heading to the dance area, the *Go-Go* Club. From its open vestibule, familiar western pop and disco beats flowed into the open bar, creating an exuberant atmosphere. Groups of people — Africans, Europeans, and Indians — sat at their respective tables nursing their drinks, relishing their appetizers, and tapping their feet to the beats, talking and laughing, while the African waiters, sweating, worked frantically, serving the resort guests.

Here was the blatant contradiction of the nation's embraced policy of socialism. But such vice was necessary — tourism was a massive industry that attracted foreigners and European holiday makers, and with them came foreign currency. The likes of Walji and Shaft were eager to grab part of that pie.

Of the African guests, many were government officials — from petty to high ranking — enjoying the fruits of graft from an underground economy fostered by the restrictive business practices, bureaucratic red tape with layers of crippling hurdles, each overcome only by a bribe. Today, Joseph was among them; before him, Mr. Kibala.

Joseph sat at the bar, alone, nursing a beer. He was dressed smartly — black slacks, pressed blue dress shirt, polished leather shoes. He looked elegant and groomed. All three walked up to him.

"Joseph, my friend, I am glad you came," said Shaft effusively, shaking his hand and introducing Walji and Miriam, who extended her soft hand, warmly smiling.

"Should we get a table?" asked Shaft.

"No I like the bar stools," said Miriam, sliding herself up the stool next to Joseph, immediately establishing her intended intimacy with Joseph. She could smell his aftershave lotion and Joseph her Arabian fragrance; he could feel her warmth when her slightly exposed thighs, above her knees, grazed against Joseph.

Shaft explained to all about how Joseph first helped him at work and how grateful he was to be an apprentice under him. Now Joseph had moved on into the realms of officialdom. All the intended accolades were to inflate Joseph's ego in the presence of Miriam, who played the part of being impressed.

Miriam put her delicate hand on Joseph's. Squeezing it, she said, "Mr. Big Shot, you owe me the first dance."

Joseph blushed and said. "Yes, yes!"

Shaft felt triumphant in a gloating way; his plan was working. He ordered some drinks — whisky and coke — for all, and said to Walji, "Let's get a table. Better now than later."

They both walked towards the dining area, a patio across the open bar, to give Miriam and Joseph their solitary moments.

At first, Joseph was tentative in conversation, and his body language spoke of nervousness, but Miriam expertly goaded him about work and trivial things, and soon, he was at ease, chatting about life in Dar, things he enjoyed, music he liked, books he read, food he relished.

Miriam was a professional social escort, her second profession. She knew what men liked to talk about. Although only form six educated, she was worldly and socially matured. She was older than Joseph, at least by five years; Joseph had just turned thirty-two, he told her.

While talking and drinking, when Joseph said something funny, Miriam would occasionally nudge Joseph with her shoulders. These few moments of closeness during conversation aroused Joseph. His lust for Miriam swelled. It was a while since he had a woman. He felt manly, and inside he grew bigger in the presence of this Arabian-Indian-looking beauty.

Just then, Walji and Shaft returned with two well dressed African women — regulars at the Africana Hotel, just waiting to be picked up by some European. They seemed to know Walji and Shaft.

Shaft introduced them: Mary — slim and tall with chiseled Somali facial features and smooth ebony skin — and Amina — short with a firm body and upright shoulders supporting her strong neck and a perfect, round face, framed between two silver loop earrings. When she smiled, her white teeth gleamed underneath her pouting, full lips.

Shaft rubbed the palms of his hands, making a flesh-grating noise, and said "We have a table, so let's eat." He then grabbed Mary's hand, while Walji escorted Amina to the dining area. Mary was a foot taller than Shaft. From this pairings of couples, it was clear to Joseph that Miriam was going to be with him — at least, for the rest of the evening. Without hesitation Miriam held his arm as Joseph stood up, and together they followed the rest of the couples.

Joseph was relieved that they had returned — Walji and Shaft had disappeared for half an hour; the private moments with Miriam had aroused Joseph. He was conscious of the slippery moistness in his underwear sipping through and staining the inseams of his trousers.

They sat at the corner table and a diligent African waiter attended them. Around them were tables with guests of all races; only a few were interracial groups (theirs being among them). The Asians mostly stuck to their own group, as did the Africans and the Europeans.

Shaft ordered the main course: filet mignon, baked potatoes, sautéed vegetables, and couple of bottles of local red wine. The conversation was strained but Walji and Shaft managed to stir it and keep it alive. Amina and Mary remained mostly quiet. Miriam talked about movies, with Joseph interjecting now and then. They talked about the war in the southern region, Fidel Castro's impending visit, Cuban medical staffing in the local health and rural clinics, and the current state of the country. Such somber topics seemed at odds in this opulent environment. But it induced among its participants an affected sense of political awareness.

But then Joseph said something remarkable that struck both Shaft and Walji: "We have taken the wrong course of action. Our policies are impractical. They will never work. Only time will tell, but by then, we will have snuffed a generation of entrepreneurial spirit so vital for commercial development."

Walji was speechless.

"Do your colleagues feel the same?" asked Walji.

"No. I don't discuss politics at work. Most feel *Mwalimu* is doing the right thing. I am a minority. My aspirations, I would say, lie with your people," Joseph said, looking directly at Walji.

"But I certainly don't like your attitudes, though. If more Asians shared their knowledge of commerce and worked alongside their African brethren, we all could benefit from it. All this muted resentment is unhealthy."

Joseph was alluding to the commercially inclined Asian community. He was slightly tipsy after a few drinks at the bar, and Miriam, at his side, spurred him to express what he felt. Shaft had never heard Joseph talk about such aspirations. In that candid outspoken sentiment, Shaft and Walji both saw an opportunity, and it only emboldened their conviction that Joseph was the right candidate: he was smart, and his quiet persona belied a guileful mind — akin to that of Walji: calculative and measured.

But in what Joseph said — and the way he put it — there was a tinge of mockery, as though he knew what was coming, and he was just playing along.

After the meal, Shaft said, laughing while chugging the last drops of wine straight from the bottle: "All that food requires some digesting now. Perhaps it is time to sweat it out on the dance floor."

Shaft led Mary by her waist, and the rest followed, with Miriam by Joseph's side, clinging on his strong arm, and Walji walked, flanked by Amina, who playfully nudged him with her elbow as they made their way to the entrance of the caved dance floor.

Inside, it was smoky and hot and dimly lit with a few recessed lights in the dome-like low ceiling. Couples — with their faces hardly definable from the throbbing disco lights — crowded the dance floor, their sweaty bodies rubbing sensually against each other, the heat from body temperatures adding to the summer heat.

The bar counter ran along one curving sidewall. Behind it, a couple of young African bartenders frantically served the demanding customers, all stretching their bills, asking for drinks. At the other end, a DJ, enclosed in his booth, focused on the dials and knobs of his musical contraption.

Miriam dragged Joseph by his hand onto the floor and put her arms around his neck; they danced closely during the slow tunes, her full breasts pressed against his moist shirt; and with her thighs slightly parted, it allowed Joseph to gently brush his throbbing bulge against her mound, and she met him with each gentle thrust, knowing he was aroused and hard and strong. This game of seduction excited Miriam: her nipples hardened and the juice of passion dampened the inside of her scanty underwear.

The rest of the night elapsed smoothly — drinking, dancing, cajoling, walking, all three couples on the beach. By closing time, all but Walji were drunk, so he managed to guide them to the parking lot where Osman awaited them. He led Joseph and Miriam to Osman's taxi, while the rest took another taxi — that was the intended plan, but Shaft was too drunk to follow through.

Miriam's flat was a two-bedroom cozy dwelling with a spacious kitchen and a small living room, with a large window that looked out onto the dirt road. Her flat was tucked away between rows of two-story buildings with shops at the bottom and flats upstairs. Down the dirt road were low-ceiling cement houses with corrugated tin roofs and open backyards from where laundry hung from makeshift lines and African women did their washing and cooking during the day.

Her flat was well furnished and inviting – sofas, coffee table, turntable, fridge, canopy bed, a phone, and ceiling fan. Surely, she could not afford the luxury items on her ticket-clerk's salary; much of the furniture and items of luxury were gifts from her well-to-do clients.

All evening, Miriam's undivided attention towards Joseph had taken him by surprise. He never thought he would end up with this Arabian-Indian beauty in her luxurious flat. These women – Arabs or Asian – were beyond his reach, inaccessible. Either you had to have plenty of money, or you had to be their kind, he thought. But Miriam had melted the racial barriers and soothed Joseph.

Miriam led him to the sofa, and said "Do you want something to drink?"

"I want you," Joseph said playfully, still giddy, pulling her down on the sofa next to him. That playful mood was induced, perhaps from all those cocktails at the open bar; normally, he was shy with women, less aggressive.

He kissed her hard on the mouth, his tongue searching and intertwining with hers, while his hand slid up her dress caressing the inside of her moist thighs, his fingers searching her wet vulva lips. She moaned and parted her legs with each probing of his fingers, as he sunk his fingers into the warm flesh, tender and moist like fresh ripe fruit.

Just then she got up, towering above him, and unfastened her dress and let it drop on the floor. She slipped out of her bra and her scanty knickers. She stood there, stark naked, grabbing her full breasts and pinching her hardened nipples with her fingertips. Then she ran her fingernails down the length of her flat stomach to her shaved mound and commanded Joseph: "Take your clothes off!"

She knew Joseph was the diminutive type from the few hours she spent with him. She knew men — all types: domineering, diminutive, rough, gentle, and insecure. And she did her sexual tricks based on that knowledge. With Joseph, she wanted to be in control, and Joseph enjoyed that part; he had always obliged to what she asked of him all evening.

Joseph rushed to undress. He was strong and big — and throbbing and dripping.

"Now kneel down and suck me, Joseph," she said firmly.

She towered above him with her legs parted, caressing her own breast with her hands. The sweet scent of her body engulfed him as he grabbed her large round buttocks with both hands and put his mouth between her parted legs. He began probing her with his tongue, darting, flicking, and nibbling, and she began to thrust herself gently, moaning, holding, and pressing his head against her parted groin.

"Oh, Joseph…oh, Joseph," she cried and moaned. She was aroused and wanted Joseph inside her mouth.

"Come on, sit down, Joseph," she commanded.

Like an obedient child, Joseph sat at the edge of the sofa, his muscular legs parted, his penis throbbing, the thin veins around it bulging. He felt the tight knot of desire inside his groin, its pressure building up.

She got on her knees teasing his cock with her straightened hair, brushing her pointed nipples against his penis. Then she gently began to stroke the length of his penis with the palm of her hands, and, slowly and surely, with measured moments, she licked it with her tongue and kissed it with her pouting moist lips, imbibing all its stickiness, while caressing his large, hairy testicles. Finally, she took him fully inside her mouth, bobbing her head up and down.

Joseph writhed in uncontrollable pleasure, pulling her down with her hair, squeezing her face between with his muscular thighs, which trembled because of the ecstatic sensation. Suddenly, she gently bit him on the penis, and Joseph let out a cry.

She stood up and pushed Joseph on the sofa and mounted him, guiding him inside her. Miriam was enjoying this; other men – older and portly – did not have Joseph's stamina. He was younger than her, strong and inexperienced, so she used him as her sex toy.

Miriam straddled him and commanded Joseph to move with her rhythms. Any minute, she could easily bring herself to an orgasm, but she held off. She wanted Joseph to take her from behind, so she stood up and got on the floor on four limbs.

Miriam then lay on her back and parted her legs wide, bringing her knees up to her chest, and guided Joseph to enter her. She had learned the ancient secrets of vaginal muscle control of flexing and contracting them around the full length of a penis; these were the secrets passed on by generations of women in the Arabian harems.

Miriam told Joseph to grab each of her bent knee; slowly at first and then rapidly, Miriam's lower body raised up to meet his forceful thrusts, her hips skillfully controlling the motions until he uncontrollably exploded inside her in trembling spasms. With each of Joseph's contraction, parts of him gushed inside Miriam.

Eventually, they made it to the bedroom at 4:00 AM, and at some point during the night, Miriam demanded Joseph for anal sex. Joseph never had anal sex with any woman before. He discovered that it excited him, thrilled him.

For the first time in his adult life Joseph experienced the taste of unbridled carnal pleasure, which would linger in his mind for days, his untiring body craving for more — every day, and Miriam would furnish it — at the price of his soul.

Govind Sharma called the following week, on Tuesday from Tanga, at the restaurant. Walji answered the phone. He was expecting Mr. Sharma's call sometime in the week.

"Ah, Walji, *bhai*. How are you?" his voice crackled on the phone.

The dreaded greeting again, Walji thought.

"Fine, Mr. Sharma."

A short silence and then, "I have good news for you. My partners want ten kilos of sugar," he said, then added, "American."

He meant they wanted US $10,000.

"*Bhai*, they also have bits of glasses from Shinyanga they want to get rid off," Mr. Sharma said.

Walji pondered for a moment. Did he mean diamonds?

"We can talk about that in person," Walji said, hoping that Mr. Sharma will get the message and cease carrying on and keep the conversation terse.

"Okay, *bhai*, I will be in town in two weeks," he said and hung up.

Walji thought regarding the diamonds, he would have to discuss it with Shaft. Earlier, he had proposed to Shaft that gemstones would be a lucrative opportunity, for it is small and easy to package and conceal, and the commissions are fat.

Walji and Shaft met at the restaurant for dinner. Shaft said Joseph had a very good time Saturday night. He told Shaft at work – Joseph had stopped by his desk before heading for the airport — to thank him for Saturday, and mentioned that he is seeing Miriam later in the week, and even confided that he liked her.

"Do you think he knows?" Walji asked

"He suspects something," Shaft said.

"We have to tell him soon. Not everything, of course. How much we can trust him is a risk we are taking. But he seems willing from what I read on Saturday. You know, the stuff he said about Asian businesses and free enterprises," said Walji.

"We have to move fast. Mr. Sharma rang today and wants ten thousand American dollars. I have about eight. We need two more. And, his clients may have some diamonds they want to smuggle out."

"Oh, how much?" asked Shaft.

"He did not say. I mean, I did not want to talk about it on the phone. He is coming here in two weeks. We will have an idea then. These might be cut or uncut diamonds, or just family jewelry. This all means you will have to plan your first trip within a month or so," said Walji, smiling.

Shaft nodded, acknowledging in his mind that finally it is all coming together. He will be able to get out and see London, the metropolis he read about in history and fiction books, saw glittering glimpses of it in the movies and postcards, heard of it from returning wealthy students with their affected manners and feigned clipped British accents. At heart – and instinctively — he was an adventurer, a risk taker, brash at times. Going to London, carrying hidden cash, and possibly diamonds, excited him, except this time he is not the good guy "Shaft" in the movies, but the bad guy.

"I want us to meet with Joseph Friday. Bring him over here after work for dinner. We should discuss his cut for each trip," said Walji.

"He would want much more than Mr. Kibala" said Shaft.

"Yes, a lot more. This is a big venture for us. And Joseph is no fool. So we have to keep him content. He can turn us in anytime. He has the key to the door through which you walk. If he decides, he can lock us up anytime," said Walji somberly.

Shaft acknowledged that he will be at Joseph's mercy at the airport during his runs. Any locals caught in possession of foreign currency exceeding US $100.00 were arrested on charges of racketeering. Such charges were akin to treason. And what happens after that, nobody knows.

"Eight thousand shillings for each trip," Walji suggested. Then, he paused for a moment and added, "and keep some room for negotiation. I have a feeling that Joseph will want more."

If Joseph resists, Walji suggested, they should up the graft, but not more than ten thousand.

On Friday evening, after work, Joseph and Shaft went for drinks at the Tusker Club on Upanga Road across from the Peugeot Motors building and then took a taxi to the Flamingo Restaurant. After Shaft's chat with Walji during the week, he arranged with Joseph to meet for dinner and he obliged.

Shaft sensed Joseph's demeanor had changed: he was open, less tentative, more willing. Over drinks at the club, Joseph revealed that his father was a carpenter and made furniture up country, in Tanga. But with government nationalization of lucrative retail enterprises, his father lost his local buyers — Asian furniture mart owners. With new policies in place to curb profit and price gauging by Asian business owners, his father had to sell his wares to government cooperatives at a reduced price, far less than what he sold for to the Asian buyers.

He told Shaft his father wished, one day, to own a small shop, a family furniture venture, where woodworks of all sorts made by his people in his village town could be sold. Joseph scoffed at the enforced stipulation of selling to government cooperatives; it was not lucrative at all, rather destructive.

Shaft pondered why Joseph told him all this. The façade of formality and seniority he had constructed at work all this time was no longer there. Had he anticipated — as Walji had questioned and what Shaft had suspected — what was to come, and was all this a sign of willingness?

Maybe, Shaft reckoned, it was easy to speak to someone of his own kind. But Joseph knew Shaft's two worlds: one African and the other Indian. It was his African persona Joseph was comfortable with.

Shaft had the natural skill and ability to present either side of himself, depending on who he was with. It was his great advantage and asset; he never confused one with the other. Over the years, he had learned to come to terms with it, and discovered how to employ this racial duality to his advantage at opportune times.

When they arrived at the restaurant, Walji was finishing his last-minute business dealings before handing it off to Mr.

Lakhani. Both were behind the counter talking, looking preoccupied.

The Friday evening crowd from the mosque down the street eventually made it to the restaurant. Asian youngsters from their community idly hung outside the mosque by the iron-grilled gates and outside on street under the neon prancing Flamingo signs of the restaurant, hoping to catch furtive glances from the fashionably dressed young women, their potential future brides, as they entered the restaurant with their families.

It was a very Indian scene inside the restaurant and about the street: the Hindi music and spicy aroma pouring out from the wide open doors, the boisterous men sitting at the tables, the measuring stares of men and women, the expensive cars hurriedly and carelessly parked on the curb, the parade of women dressed in resplendent and sequined saris.

Unspoken signs of Indian proprietorship and exclusivity marked the streets around the mosque and the restaurant. Sometimes outsiders kept away on Friday and Sunday nights; they dubbed it as "Asian Night," just as Sundays in many cinemas in Dar were exclusively for Indian movies.

Walji wanted this Asiatic backdrop, a world intimately and historically woven into the country's cultural landscape, yet alien and distant to Joseph, to propose a new partnership as a gesture of initiation.

From behind the counter, Walji gestured to Shaft to take the corner table, away from the crowd, providing privacy and yet a panoramic view of the dining area. A few minutes later, he joined them.

"Ah *ndugu*, Joseph, welcome!" he said, firmly shaking Joseph's hand.

"I hope you like Indian food. This is the best in town," Walji boasted.

"I have never been to this restaurant before," said Joseph, smiling, "but I do not doubt that it is the best," acknowledged Joseph.

"Good then. I will order. I am afraid there is no alcohol served here. It is owned by a Muslim," said Walji apologetically.

"But you and Shaft" — here Joseph used Shaft instead of Shafiq — "drink like fishes," said Joseph quizzically.

"Oh we are just bad and evil," said Walji.

Walji called out one of his waiters and ordered the specials for today — mutton birayani, garlic chicken curry, and chapatti and some samosas as appetizers.

Joseph looked around, absorbing the cultural nuances. Apart from the waiters and Shaft, he was about the only African in the restaurant. He heard other tongues being spoken around him at the tables. A few women at various tables glanced in his direction, their stares blank, and their expression dull with boredom; they were in a crowd with other couples, disengaged from their partner's manly conversation.

Moments later, an old, frail-looking lady, part of her head covered with a frayed and flimsy *patchedi*, gingerly approached their table.

"Ma," called out Walji tenderly, "Saidi will bring the food for you."

"No, *bheta*, I was going home from the mosque. I will pick it up and go," she said slowly, heavily breathing, like someone catching their breath after an asthma attack. She looked frail and withering.

Walji masked his pain watching her mother's suffering. He knew she was dying from old age and a terminal lung disease that affected her breathing. About the only thing local doctors at the Aga Khan Hospital could do was subscribe antibiotics and pain killers; they had failed to diagnose her illness. They suspected lung cancer, but more tests were required they said, and she would have to travel abroad, which was not a viable financial option. So Walji let nature take its brutal course.

"Ma, this is my friend, Joseph," Walji introduced him.

Out of respect for the elderly, Joseph got up, and before he could say anything, she put her hand on his head and said, "Sit down, sit down. Come home sometime, and eat with us. Alnoor's friends are my children," she said, her eyes misty and dull from the enlarged cataracts. She was breathless again.

She had the habit of inviting Walji's friends home for food. She loved to cook, but with her debilitating illness, she could barely do any work; her ailment sapped her energy. All day she slept, and later in the day, she would walk gingerly to the mosque with Shaft's parents. All meals were delivered to the complex by the restaurant worker, Saidi. He sometimes tended to her, for which Walji paid him extra.

That was her constrained life; and she knew that her days were numbered – as did Walji and Shaft.

Walji got up and asked Saidi to escort her across the street to the flat. Shaft went with them and said he will be right back.

Ma reminded Joseph of his mother in the village. He thought mothers are same everywhere: at a deeper level, the selfless love for their children is universal. He restrained himself from saying anything complimentary.

"She does not have much time. She is going to die soon," Walji said wistfully, looking in her direction as she walked gingerly — flanked by Saidi and Shaft — out the open restaurant doors.

"Do you own this restaurant?" asked Joseph, changing the course of the conversation, steering away from Walji's mother's brief appearance.

"No, no. I am a worker, like everybody else. I manage it. You see that portly man behind the counter?" Walji pointing to Mr. Lakhani, "he owns it. I have been working for him for a few years now. I live across the street. It is perfect. There is a lodging house upstairs that I manage as well."

Joseph was in Walji's world — the restaurant, his ailing mother, and his people. In his second meeting with Walji, Joseph saw another side of Walji, a human side, a tender one.

A moment later, Shaft joined them. He said Ma was fine, eating with his parents. Finally, the delicious food arrived, the aroma filling the air above the table.

Walji looked at Shaft, who nodded.

"Joseph," Walji said with feigned low voice, "Shaft and I have a business proposition for you. We think we all three can benefit from it. But we require your help."

Walji paused for a moment, looked around the dining area and continued.

"You see all these people here today? Some are very wealthy. Among them are businessmen from the interior who lodge upstairs. Business is in their blood. The opportunities that you and I don't see, they do. They pick up a business venture, like a dog picks up a scent.

"But you know how the business climate has changed in the country. Our government has ruined and snuffed that flame of flourishing enterprise. But they are survivors, and they will find other ways. Work around the obstacles. Take their business elsewhere. This is where we three come into play and can facilitate things. We can be the middlemen who can work the invisible strings."

"How?" asked Joseph, showing curiosity and interest.

"They need to buy merchandise outside this country and bring it back inside and sell it. But as you know, one needs capital outside. Someone has to help them to get the initial capital abroad. Once enough capital is established abroad, it can be used to purchase the goods which can be shipped back here and sold," explained Walji.

"And you being the man in charge of the customs, can facilitate the export and import," said Walji, reaching for the samosas.

"But that is illegal!" said Joseph.

"What is not illegal, Joseph?" interjected Shaft.

"We cannot turn a blind eye to the underground economy of bribes and kickbacks. It is what keeps all those party bureaucrats happy and content. If you don't do it, someone else will. When opportunity knocks on the door, and if you don't take it, it will move on to knock someone else's door and they will seize it," said Walji.

He chose his words carefully. Always, he asserted at the right moment; always he employed the effective tone, justifying his proposition, even subtly suggesting an ultimatum.

There is more of your kind out there Walji was insinuating. Finding them will not be an issue; it is how things have worked for the last few years — the endemic corruption at all levels of the society. Every African — like any human elsewhere in the continent — wants the same comforts of life that he sees his fellow countryman is bestowed with: a good house, a nice car, fashionable clothes, good food, and access to good health and education for his progeny, in the city as well as in the villages.

"I will be breaking the law," said Joseph.

"No, we three will be breaking the law," said Shaft.

"What is you want me to do?" asked Joseph

"Facilitate the imports and exports. You see, now and then, I will be going on trips abroad. After a few of my trips, containers of goods will arrive at the port. You will be notified to ensure that they get delivered to their owners without problems," said Shaft.

"And for every trip Shaft takes, we pay you eight thousand shillings," added Walji.

Joseph absorbed the choreographed proposition from Walji and Shaft. He knew that if he accepted their proposition, his life will change, for better or worse. For better — as the extra income would help his father. Ultimately, he knew that the gains will amass; later he could ask more, for he was the facilitator, and he knew they needed him. Without him, the "import and export" would not materialize, unless they found someone else. But he thought he should not be greedy. He should take as it comes.

"And what do I get for clearing the goods?" asked Joseph.

Walji said: "We can revisit it later. It is not in my hands. That portion belongs to the people who will receive the goods. Depends on the goods, you know. But it will be more, a lot more. All that is still open, Joseph, because it is not there yet. But it will happen over time."

Walji broke the somber conversation and jokingly said "We will starve and the food will get cold if we don't eat it."

Each grabbed a plate and helped themselves to a hearty portion of the assorted dishes. The crowd around was boisterous — kids walked about the dining areas, unsupervised; men broke out laughing aloud at dirty jokes exchanged at their tables. At one table alongside the window, youngsters sang along to the tunes of a hit Hindi movie, *Kabhi Kabhi*. Such chorus singing was not uncommon among Asian young men, in bars, in Indian restaurants, or at parties. It was their way of expressing passion, often love to a secret beloved in the crowd; these were borrowed gestures from Hindi movies, the emotions exaggerated and replayed like scenes and dialogues from their favorite actors.

Joseph was amused by all that surrounded him, new experiences for all his senses.

"How often will be your trips?" asked Joseph, looking at Shaft, while eating his chapatti. He imitated Walji's technique of curling and scooping the thick chicken curry with the pieces of ripped chapatti.

"First, not as often, maybe once every six months. But later, perhaps as often as once every two months," said Shaft.

Joseph said, "If I consider this proposition, my life will change. My conscious has to accept this. I have never done this before. Your people are the ones who will benefit most from this. Not me. If I am willing to corrupt my soul and betray my country, I want more," Joseph asserted.

"Betray *our* country. We are part of it as well," corrected Walji.

"How much more?" asked Shaft.

"I want fifteen thousand for each of Shaft's trip. I will guarantee his safe departure," emphasized Joseph.

Walji sighed and looked at Shaft, who knew what to say.

"Joseph, we can do ten thousand at most. Perhaps after a couple of successful trips, we can bring it up to fifteen thousand. We all are middlemen here. We don't get as much either. Both of us are willing to cut our commission to add to your desired amount. But ten thousand for now is the best we can do," said Shaft with a convincing and assertive tone, implying in no uncertain terms to Joseph: *take it or leave it.*

Joseph pondered for a while and then acquiesced. He asked that half the payment should be made before and the other half after Shaft's safe departure. The terms were agreeable to all parties.

Joseph had let Miriam bewitch his heart and body; now, he let these enterprising confidence men corrupt his soul. But he never doubted that anything bad will come from it. He justified it, being in the civil service, knowing how things got done. Africans like him in powerful positions of influence, across all sectors of the civil service, exercised their authority and accepted kickbacks of all sorts. It was an accepted way of life, like drinking in public; meager wages never met with the rising inflation of merchandise.

Just as it was natural for the Asian to hand out bribes, so it was for the African to accept them. And that was the unspoken and accepted way of business transactions between the government sector — dominated by Africans in power at all levels — and the private sector — controlled by the Asians. Each supported the other, and together, it formulated an underground symbiotic world, which overtime became endemic.

The restaurant was an integral part of their underground world. Through its open, welcoming doors, first entered Mr. Kibala, then Mr. Sharma, and then Joseph; and what motivated these middlemen was human greed. Brokering was their means of survival, their livelihood, where other opportunities were limited, curtailed.

At the surface, the serenity of the restaurant entertained and nourished one set of clientele; beneath its veils of the people who ran it, under the large framed picture on the wall of the benevolent *Mwalimu*, the father of African socialism, another set of distant, invisible clients' demands were fulfilled. The irony of it all escaped everybody!

After the meal, Walji suggested that they celebrate the beginnings of a new and enterprising venture, so the three took a taxi to the New Africa Hotel for drinks.

In his flat in Kinondoni, after the drinks, Joseph reflected over the evening events. He sat on his firm bed, just below the mosquito bed net. A naked bulb illuminated his bedroom. The walls were bare, marked with holes and dust. Along one wall was his dresser with a mirror, and next to it, a small cupboard with sliding doors for his clothing. His uniform hung on makeshift hooks, made from nails driven into the walls. In the center of the room was a small coffee table, matched in finish to the bedside table, on which lay glossy magazines and weekly newspapers, mouthpieces of the government policies.

He shared this typical African dwelling with two other roommates in this African district: a simple, corrugated tin roof plopped atop crisscrossed wooden beams, on top of four cement walls, covering three bedrooms, a living room, and a small open backyard with washing area and a toilet.

He looked at the walls, self-conscious, and thought: It was not where he would want to bring Miriam; he would be ashamed of the comparison. Her flat was so lavish by local standards, full of amenities; his looked dull and shabby. She was only a ticketing clerk, and he, a government official in power – that was the impression Shaft had cultivated for her. But he was an officer in customs, not senior enough. Only supervisors and managers were provided with houses usurped from Asians with multiple homes: part of a government policy of property appropriation for redistribution.

He entertained and romanced the idea of additional money: with it, he thought, he would upgrade and improve the décor of his room and part of the house with furniture from his father and spend it on Miriam. In his mind, he replayed the delicious carnal moments with her from last week and the mood intoxicated him, dissolving his guilt.

The guilt stemmed from what the government had provided for: it paid for his formative education, followed by a diploma in business administration at the local college, which landed him a job at the immigration office as a clerk, where he was a diligent employee — loyal, but not an intellectual. What transpired politically in the country had little appeal to him; its spirit and ideas did not stick with him. The African clamors of liberation and self-reliance, espoused by the *Mwalimu*, escaped him; instead, the vainglory of money — and its power — embraced and enchanted him. Like others of his lot, he fell prey to the likes of Walji and Shaft.

His mind drifted away with thoughts of Miriam, and the events of the evening faded away. Only the idea of money lingered, which lulled him to sleep.

Outside, crickets chirped and the bats fluttered above mango trees on the wide, empty lot. Now and then, the high yellow moon withdrew behind puffs of dense clouds, and the darkness, amidst the city district, descended on the surroundings streets.

M iriam dressed casually for the evening — a *Kitenge* skirt, an open neck black blouse, which contrasted with the light colored African patterns on her skirt. The low cut on her blouse exposed her cleavage, teasingly. She had her curly hair tucked in a tight bun, secured by the two pencil-thin wooden sticks; parts of hair showed tinges of reddish-brown from henna.

Joseph had arranged to meet her in Upanga at the Sea View Hotel. The name was deceiving; there was no view of the Indian Ocean, but behind the main hotel building, outside on the open dance floor, at night, the air smelled of salty washed up seaweed from nearby Indian Ocean; and during high tides, sounds from breaking and splashing waves against cliff rocks disrupted the stillness of the quiet nights.

Joseph arrived early, anxious, and grabbed a table on the patio, facing the dance floor, encircled with naked, colored bulbs suspended from a loose wire running along its perimeter attached to wooden poles. He was nervous, so he drank a couple of Tuskers — they were tepid; the refrigerators at the hotel bar were decommissioned, for there were no parts available locally for replacement. Getting a cold beer was a luxury at some of these clubs.

The hotel was owned by a Greek and an African government official. It catered to all races, but mostly Africans patronized it on Fridays and Saturdays; often, you saw a smatter of brown and white faces — not of Africa but now part of it — merged with black faces.

Its atmosphere was African; the crowd gathered late, after dinner, for most of the dancing commenced after 11:00 PM. Like most African clubs, first comes all the drinking with boisterous palavering, followed by the sweaty bodies gyrating and dancing into early morning hours.

And even here, inside the hotel foyer, you couldn't escape the smiling face of *Mwalimu* peering at you from its large framed picture, a nagging reminder of what the country stands for, what your duty should be. But those who came here were not intellectuals, not adherents of government doctrines; they were petty government workers, civil servants, clerks. For most, this was an escape from the harsh realities of a country going under change. It was a choice made for them, not opted by them. Whatever their wages were (and a little extra extorted from bribes), they were wasted here.

Miriam spotted Joseph at the table; they greeted – a handshake, an embrace, a pat on the back from her. Greetings were physical: touching and holding of hands — sometimes while conversing for long periods; it is a gesture of warmth and acceptance.

"I came here once, a while back. I loved it. They play Congolese music," said Miriam excitedly, looking around. There were few occupied tables with men and women casually talking.

"I thought you only liked western and Indian music," said Joseph.

"Not true. I like everything I can dance to," replied Miriam, reproachfully.

Joseph beckoned an African waiter leaning idly against the open doorway. He was dressed in a white uniform – a long-sleeved jacket, frayed at the wrists, and trousers short in length that exposed parts of his naked feet and thin rubber slippers; other waiters similarly dressed hung around the bar, awaiting summons.

Joseph ordered a couple of beers. All along, the waiter stared down at Miriam's blouse; she gave him a raised eyebrow look, and he switched his attention to Joseph.

At the far end of the open dance area, an African cook was preparing the grill; next to it, on the wooden table, he laid uncooked meat: cut-up pieces of goat shoulders and legs, beef ribs, chopped chicken, potatoes, and raw corn.

The waiter took his time. Finally, the beers arrived. The waiter casually placed the two warm beers on the table, plopped the glass next to each bottle, and asked Joseph for the cash.

"We should order some *nyama* later," Joseph said, pointing in the direction of the grill.

"Of course, how can you drink without *mbuzi?*" agreed Miriam.

She knew what to say and when to say, always putting Joseph at ease, always leading him — in conversation as well as in the bedroom. It was natural for her, just as it is natural and intuitive for a Japanese geisha.

They chatted about mundane things — work, rising prices, shortages of ordinary items: milk, butter, toilet paper, items once taken for granted, now only acquired by contacts. They lamented how it had come down to who you knew where, that is how you got what you wanted.

Soon, after a few rounds of drinks, Joseph ordered some food from the grill. They ate, drank, and joined the rest on the dance floor.

So went the rest of the evening, both in tight bodily embrace on the dance floor, each deriving sensual pleasure from the other's body, as the Congolese music rocked them all.

Finally, it climaxed at Miriam's house, just as it had the previous week with Miriam in total control in the bedroom, demanding, giving and taking pleasure, and Joseph obliging to it all.

The quintessential Sunday afternoon lethargy and stillness descended onto Dar after the 2:00 PM car ban, a government-enforced measure to conserve fuel. Only taxis, diplomatic cars, and notable government vehicles were exempted from it.

Before the deadline, the town buzzed with traffic: cars, trucks, motorcycles driving hurriedly from Oyster Bay to their final destinations; then silence; occasionally a jingle of a bicycle bell disrupted the quiet streets.

Two weeks had elapsed since Mr. Sharma rang Walji at the restaurant. Last night, while Walji was out, Mr. Sharma left a note for Walji with Mr. Lakhani, asking Walji for a rendezvous at 2:00 PM in Mr. Sharma's guest house room.

Walji knocked on the door of the single room on the second floor shortly after 2:00 PM. Mr. Sharma answered the door promptly and invited him inside. Walji was familiar with all the rooms on that floor: he had managed the renovation of the rooms with modern décor — bedside tables and reading lamps, short, pastel-colored curtains matching the moss green walls, bed nets, paintings on the wall, guest table, and chairs.

"Good to see you, *bhai*!" said Mr. Sharma.

Walji nodded and took the empty seat by the guest table; the other chairs had disheveled clothes, worn from previous day, on it. On the table, a few empty beer bottles encircled couple of glasses. A familiar faint perfume scent — used by many local prostitutes — lingered in the air combined with stale stench from empty beer bottles.

Walji reckoned Mr. Sharma had an overnight guest, probably a prostitute picked up from one of the town bars. He had made no effort to conceal it; on the untidy bed, on top of the pillow, lay a red, lacy woman's underwear, the expensive kind, one probably imported from abroad — none of the Chinese ones available in the stores had any sex appeal design to it; they were meant for the workers.

Perhaps Mr. Sharma had bought it for his companion; or perhaps he was being a sugar daddy to some young African school girl, like many men in power with money did. At the bars or clubs at night, it was not unusual to see men in power in the company of enamored schoolgirls.

"I have good news for you. Looks like we can do business," said Mr. Sharma, picking up the empty beer bottles and putting them in the wastebasket underneath the table.

"Do you have the ten thousand?" asked Mr. Sharma.

"Yes, dollars," replied Walji.

"Good. That will do," said Mr. Sharma.

"Now, we have to discuss the diamonds," said Mr. Sharma with a serious tone, wasting no time.

Walji shifted his body and leaned forward, placing his hands on the table, fingers crossed, suggesting earnest interest.

"My clients have twenty pieces of cut diamonds, each 1.5 carats. They want them safely delivered to Dubai. Good quality; well-cut. And another client wants $10,000.00 delivered to London. As you can see, my friend, this is start of a good business. We all can do well. The future is bright for us.

"What is going to be your commission for the gems?" asked Mr. Sharma.

He reached for his trademark Indian *pan* and put it inside his mouth and started chewing it. It was a sign for Walji to start talking.

A couple of weeks ago after Mr. Sharma hinted about the diamonds on the phone, Walji had done research about the diamonds at the library. He had read everything to know about them so he would appear knowledgeable while conversing or enquiring about them. He had also visited a couple of Asian jewelers about town who dealt with diamonds.

"Surely, it will be a percentage of its street value. As you know, diamonds come in many cuts. Are they all round brilliant cuts?" asked Walji.

Mr. Sharma nodded. A mouthful of beetle juice from the *pan* prevented him from saying anything. A moment later, he reached for the wastebasket underneath the table and let out a streaming spit of red beetle juice.

Always, Walji tolerated this nuisance. Always, he managed to disguise his disgust.

"A round brilliant cut diamond. I mean, a well-cut 1.5 carat diamond by some of the top cutters in South Africa, London, New York or Antwerp, can run $5000.00. Cutters are rare here, and we don't have the industry in this country. These gems must have been cut in South Africa, DeBeers maybe," added Walji, recalling his research.

"There is an underground cartel down south. It is rumored that part of the liberation guerilla movement is financed by this cartel," added Walji

Mr. Sharma seemed surprised at Walji's response. It was a reminder to Mr. Sharma that underneath Walji's boyish and handsome looks — about which he had commented before — was steely shrewdness. He was not dealing with an amateur, Mr. Sharma told himself.

"What is your cut?" asked Mr. Sharma.

"Twenty percent of the total street value and that includes everybody's cut on my side," said Walji.

Walji knew it was high, but he thought he would give himself plenty of room for negotiations.

"*Bhai*, it is lot of money," said Mr. Sharma with a tone of overplayed disbelief.

"Well, your clients can sell these abroad for a lot of money. The street value for this popular cut 1.5 carat is close to $4000.00 — maybe $5000.00. I am taking into account my risks, and of the courier who will do the running of these to Dubai. Plus, you don't have to pay me in pounds or dollars. Local currency will do," retorted Walji.

Payment in local currency was an attractive option. And that was enticing for Mr. Sharma — and would be so for his clients. Walji knew Mr. Sharma's clients had plenty of local currency to disburse; what good was it to them stashed away? Any moment soon, rumors revealed, the government was intent on changing the currency, invalidating the old currency; the only way to obtain the new currency was to exchange the old with the new at the national bank, and account for it. That way, the government could confiscate large sums of unaccounted monies hoarded by many local businessmen over the years.

"But the street value is a bit high for this. Would you settle for the fifteen percent over the cost of the stones, *bhai*?" asked Mr. Sharma, tilting his head to the left.

Mr. Sharma's clients had bought them from a South African middleman for equivalent of $2000.00 dollars for each stone; it was a good deal for them. Mr. Sharma knew that the street value was close to $5000.00, so they would still be making enough profit.

"I will be honest with you. My clients paid $1800.00 for it," Mr. Sharma lied.

Walji absorbed numbers and made some mental calculations. It was still a good offer. It was probably the best one to come his way, far more lucrative than passport deals and the currency trading. This was the nascent of what was to come. A few more of these transactions this year and Shaft and Walji would be set for grander ventures; they would have capital.

But Walji had to play the game, show dissatisfaction, convey reluctance, and eventually, agree to it. Both seemed content, like two business partners starting a mutually profitable venture.

"But there is one thing I have to be assured of — the merchandise has to be validated by a neutral jeweler as genuine. The business of stones, like currency, is risky. It has its uncertain elements, and as you know, we both want everybody to be happy and not surprised at the last minute," asserted Walji.

"Oh, *bhai*, no problem. You pick the jeweler and we go there before I hand them to you," said Mr. Sharma assuredly, "Now how soon can it be done?"

"In the next two or three weeks," said Walji. "My courier has to make travel arrangements for Dubai and London. I will need details of your contacts there," added Walji.

They settled on terms of payment: the full amount would be paid in cash, in local currency, to Walji on spot after a confirmation from Shaft and the contact in Dubai is made in tandem over a phone. The confidential details of the contact — and rendezvous methods — would be revealed the day of the departure after Walji and Mr. Sharma validated the authenticity of diamonds with the local jeweler.

"I will call you next week and confirm the departure date. It will be close to the Christmas holiday. Perfect for traveling — a busy time at the airport, security could be relaxed," smiled Walji.

In the last hour, from the summer heat outside, the air in the room got stuffy and oppressive. Both Walji and Mr. Sharma felt the discomfort.

Walji got up and shook Mr. Sharma's hand and bid farewell, and like a good businessman, he assured Mr. Sharma: "You won't be disappointed doing business with me."

He smiled and left Mr. Sharma sitting on the chair. On the way down to the restaurant, Walji thought everything was moving rapidly. The anxiety came to him in waves, but like a good surfer, he managed to ride them.

He had to sort out the operational logistics. It was his first major deal, and he wanted it executed smoothly. His mind raced, arranging and rearranging the order of tasks ahead of the run. He made mental notes and was preoccupied for the rest of the day.

Immediately, he had to get hold of Shaft to make arrangements for a trip to Dubai and London the week of December 18ᵗʰ — it wasn't going to be easy, Walji knew, to get a flight during the holiday season; but Miriam, working for a travel agency, could make it happen.

Walji had to design clever ways to conceal the stones for Shaft, not so much for the Dar airport customs, but for the destination. After all, Shaft would be carrying merchandise worth $100,000 and $10,000 in cash. And none of it was going to be declared to the port of entry custom officials.

Then there was the unknown rendezvous with the contacts in Dubai and London to coordinate. It all had to be at a convenient time, for all parties present. Much of it will depend on Shaft's arrival times, but he dismissed that worry for now.

He walked briskly across the street in the bright light of the afternoon towards Shaft's flat. Shaft had taken his parents to an afternoon Indian movie, as he often did on Sundays.

Walji went across to his flat, fished a piece of paper from his shirt pocket, jotted down a note for Shaft and left it at Shaft's door step, asking him to meet at 7:00 PM for dinner at the restaurant.

Then he went home to check on his ailing mother, who was asleep in her bed, her frail body covered under a soft white linen sheet. Her wheezy and laborious breathing punctured the Sunday afternoon silence of the room. Walji's nagging fear of one day walking into a silent room with his mother's lifeless body on her bed had transformed into a moment of anticipation. He had accepted what was unavoidable; her prolonged suffering grew on him, and it constrained him.

In ways Walji never comprehended, she was his center of existence, his only link to the dissolving past. With the death of his mother, like that of Walji's grandparents, a slice of history will perish. Yet, his lot never examined the past to see their future, never inquired to asses their relation to the present. How could they? Nothing was ever recorded; they lived only for the moment, without a clear idea of the past, as survivors in a political landscape not of their making, nor within their grasp; they were on the fringes of it; and some of their lot were the descendants of jettisoned laborers from a larger historical event originated elsewhere for rulers far away.

For Joseph, the past lay in the village elders, oral traditions of his tribe, passed down with generations, recited at (and during) many village gatherings. He was of the African soil, not made to come to the African soil. He had a patch of land to return to, lay claim to as part of his African inheritance, so easily and readily. If city life failed him, village life will embrace him. Joseph never doubted the comfort of this safety net. He could easily return to the ways of his ancestors.

Not so for Walji. Walji was a historical castaway, and all the bridges to ancestral land — India — were mirages. The idea of an inherited or claimed piece of land in the African interior (inherited because of one's tribal ancestors) was alien.

What Walji had revolved around him — the street, the restaurant (and its shadowy dealings), his community (now under massive emigration), and the insecurities of a disenfranchised minority in a rapidly shifting political landscape.

Like many of his kind, his political loyalty remained doubtful. His inscrutable loyalty was to wealth – and the ways of amassing it; it was his security, and that of many like him. That incorrigible greed stemmed from depths of insecurity and his place in the world (or lack of it). Wealth grants status; status furnishes acceptance; and acceptance instills a sense of belonging.

Walji sat on the couch in the small sitting room. On the coffee table was Sunday's paper. He only read the sports page for football results of the African Cup, underway in Nigeria. His favorite team, Simba Sports Club, was playing the Nigerian Eagles in the quarter finals. Now and then, to appear portentous in conversations with his European expatriate friends at the New Africa Hotel, he would read about the local politics.

From where he sat, he could hear her mother's faint wheezing sounds as her lungs drew air for life. After a time of reading the newspaper and skimming the political headlines, he fell asleep.

Shaft returned with his parents after the matinee show. While his parents went to the mosque down the street, he walked to the flat where a note attached to his door from Walji awaited him. It was 7:15 PM, so he walked briskly across the dingy courtyard, past the wooden gateway, and across the street to the restaurant.

Mr. Lakhani was managing from behind the counter. The crowd was sparse. Their eyes met, and Mr. Lakhani gestured with his hands, asking "Where is Walji?" pointing to his wristwatch. Shaft reckoned he should check the flat. It was not usual for Walji to be late for work. Walji was always punctual. Had something happened to Ma? Shaft feared, so he quickly returned to the housing complex to check upon Walji.

He firmly knocked on Walji's door. The door was ajar and it gently swung open from the force of his knocks. Walji was asleep on the sofa, newspaper on the floor. Shaft heard Ma's faint breathing sounds from the open doorway, and he was relieved.

Shaft smiled and tenderly slapped Walji on the head a couple of times, ruffling his voluminous silky black hair and said: "Man, you are late for work. Mr. Lakhani wants to go to the mosque."

Walji jumped up and told Shaft to tell Mr. Lakhani he will be there shortly and instructed Shaft to wait for him there. They had to talk. It was always that somber tone that Walji employed: "We have to talk."

Shaft knew it meant either progress or change of plans, and so he obliged and did what his partner-in-crime suggested.

After some time, Walji showed up to relieve Mr. Lakhani, who was visibly agitated. He had missed his first evening prayers. Mr. Lakhani would entertain prostitutes in the guest house upstairs, drink alcohol, furnish gambling rooms for a commission, condone all the wheeling and dealing before his eyes, lie and cheat, yet he loathed missing his first evening prayers. Such hypocrisy was endemic among many of his lot.

Oddly, a couple of tables were occupied by a group of young self-absorbed Europeans, mostly Scandinavians. On Sunday and Friday nights, after the mosque, a crowd comprised mostly of Asians paraded the street and occupied the restaurant, but this European group must have been new in town: recent arrivals, unaware of the "Asian Night."

For the last couple of years, aid from Nordic countries poured in; they were the largest donors and ardent supporters of *Mwalimu's* policies; and with monies from the countries of colder climes came the idealistic young volunteers, who were here more so for the African adventure, experience, than for the realization of the socialist ideals learned from volumes of academic papers written on Africa. In short time, the harsh realities of African life would dissolve their idealism, and they would achingly yearn to return to the comforts of their world.

After some time, Walji and Shaft sat for dinner, and ordered the Sunday specials – garlic lamb curry with leavened bread and rice. They had about a half hour before the mosque crowd gathers about, and the street and restaurant transforms into little India.

Walji told Shaft about Mr. Sharma's visit that afternoon: the diamond run to Dubai, the cut they had agreed upon, and the tentative travel dates. What remained to be decided were the logistical arrangements of the rendezvous in Dubai and London, and the concealment of the "packages" – money and gemstones.

"Dubai?" said Shaft, disapprovingly.

"Yes. Duty-free port, city of jewelry and foreign currency trading, the Hong Kong of Middle East," said Walji smugly, and then he added, "And we can be part of that network. It is one of the most lucrative underground markets in the world, my friend. I heard that the custom officials are more concerned about alcohol and drugs smuggled into the city than money, gold, and diamonds."

"So we have to figure out the best way to slip the goods in undetected," said Walji.

"False bottoms," replied Shaft.

"We cut through a layer of my big platform shoes, cut holes in them to embed the diamonds, and nail it back in," elaborated Shaft.

"And the money?" asked Walji.

"There are numerous ways. If they are big bills, sew them into your jackets or make a false bottom inside a suit case. Ten thousand in US $100.00 bills is not bulky. Are they $100.00 bills?" asked Shaft.

Walji nodded.

"Well, don't worry. I will handle this. After all, it is me who is doing the run, and I have to be confident," said Shaft.

"And have Miriam help you get the tickets. Remember, the departing day must be Monday or Wednesday. Once we have the date, we can arrange a meeting with Joseph. Give him his advance. Keep him happy," said Walji.

"How do you feel?" asked Walji.

"Dubai and London? Both sound intriguing," said Shaft, giving his trademark smirk.

"Is Dubai going to be a regular run?" asked Shaft.

"Not sure. I think Mr. Sharma is testing the waters. If this goes well, and his contacts over there work out well, this might be a regular run. Of course, we cannot be very frequent otherwise the Dubai Customs officials will sniff something. We will have to think of official ways for the trip, like a business visit. But most importantly, let's make this one happen. Everything depends on the success of this one," added Walji in his typical grave purposeful tone.

"Right, right, no problem," said Shaft.

Often, Shaft felt Walji's cautionary approach petulant, patronizing, but tolerable. In many ways, they complemented each other; they needed each other. Both knew what was necessary for the success of this operation, both were committed to see it through — Walji working the logistics, Shaft executing the plan, doing the field work.

Inside the restaurant, a crowd from the mosque began to flow in. Outside, boisterous Asian youngsters gathered around the street. Soon, the restaurant buzzed with a cacophony of tongues and melodious Hindi music, mixed with clicks and clacks of the silverware and the dishes in the kitchen. A strong aroma of delicious Indian spices wafted from the kitchen and lingered in the dining area, providing a foretaste of the savory dishes. The worries of Africa dissolved here, and for a short period, life continued as it used to be: Africa in the background and transported India — in its sacrosanct form — to the forefront.

Outside the restaurant along the street, some African street vendors laid their goods on sisal mats, always vigilant of the raiding government militia staging their ambush; the government discouraged these enterprising practices and sent militia to chase them off, often confiscating their merchandise while the vendors fled; and those apprehended were labeled indolent and were whisked off in government jeeps to government "collective farms" in the interior to toil.

Next day, at lunch break, Shaft walked to Miriam's office on Samora Michel Avenue, across from the roundabout with the *Askari* statue. Earlier that morning, he called and gave her the desired departure dates. She said she would have a reasonable idea around lunch time what was available, but it might be tight, she hinted; she might have to "bump" somebody.

Miriam had charted a flight route for Shaft: Dar to Dubai (Air Tanzania) and Dubai to London (U.A.E Airways) and back again the same route, same carrier, leaving Dar on Wednesday December 22, arriving back in Dar on January 4th. He would not be able to leave Dubai for London until December 27th. Because of the holiday season, there were no seats available on any carrier out of Dubai to any cities in Europe that week.

Shaft had no choice but to accept it. The drama of the travel abroad began to register with him as he held the tickets in his hand. Never before had he traveled overseas; he only provided people with passports that enabled them to travel. The anxiety and fear of the courier run and the job at hand were dissolved by the excitement of going overseas.

On the way back to work, he thought of the two cities — Dubai and London. What would they be like? But his thoughts of inquiry were answered by preconceived images of London made up by films, glorious metropolis, modern, with smartly dressed men in pinstriped suits and umbrellas and pretty women in fashionable clothes, strutting up and down orderly pavements, red double-decker buses, and traditional black taxis on the roads. Of Dubai nothing came to mind, no image of landscape or people, only references in Indian movies of a lucrative port in the oil-rich Arab world, heaven for gold smugglers. But he would have to know more of Dubai.

From his work at the immigration office, Shaft knew travelers to the United Arab Emirates required a transit visa if the onward flight to the next destination was within four days. He had his passport issued to him a while back when Walji had spoken of the runs. When he arrived at the office, he rang the U.A.E Embassy and was told by a woman with a polite and neutral accent that he would require a valid onward ticket by a carrier operated in U.A.E and a valid passport. Normally, she told Shaft over the phone, the transit visas are issued immediately and only during morning hours.

The next morning, after breakfast at the restaurant when he told Walji about the developments, Shaft took the taxi to the U.A.E embassy and acquired his visa. The process was unimpeded. The woman who spoke to him on the phone attended to him; he recognized the neutral accent. She was young, full bodied — an Arab, not African Arab from the coastal area, but Arab from Arabia. Her mature voice belied her age. It was the voice one hears on the radio – lucid, every word enunciated, rightly intoned where necessary. Shaft wondered if all women in Dubai looked like her, dressed like her, spoke like her.

Shaft asked for tourist guides to Dubai. She pointed in the direction of a small doorway leading to wooden shelf with brochures, pamphlets and thin booklets, all loudly promoting the glamour of Dubai. Shaft grabbed one of each. On the way back, he scanned through the literature. He was struck and impressed with pictures of swanky buildings with glass exteriors, clustered skyscrapers and complex structures — so modern and different from Dar. The imagery energized him. Now he had an image of what Dubai may look like, just as he had an image of London.

What remained to be accomplished was designing the false bottoms — one in the suitcase to conceal money, the other in the platform shoe in which to embed diamonds. It was a delicate task. Shaft would not entrust anyone with it. Only the courier, Shaft told himself, should have knowledge of it.

There were a number of stores in town and in Kariako that sold suitcases. He visited them all, looking for the right size, with enough depth, and a slight trough, just couple of inches deep, running along the edges of its bottom perimeter. At last, he found one – black plastic encasing inside and checkered black and red-colored square cloth pattern on the outside — at an Arab store; he bought two of the same kind.

Next, he visited a couple of cobblers with a pretense of resoling his worn out platform shoes and asked them detailed questions about the procedure. He made mental notes of the required workmanship, raw materials and tools — a leather cutter-knife, special leather glue, some ½ inch nails, and a scrubber. The cobblers told him that most platform shoes have a second layer of sole that is usually glued onto it that can be pried out.

Afterwards, he visited the hardware store recommended by the cobblers and was pleasantly surprised that what he desired was available. Triumphant in his endeavors for the day, Shaft took the taxi home and skipped work that day.

He met with Walji mid-afternoon at the restaurant and requested a guest room where he could work on the task at hand. Walji obliged and gave him the keys to a shabby room, designated for renovation, on the first floor at the end of the terrace.

For the rest of the evenings that week after work, the dingy room became Shaft's secret workshop. There, he delicately constructed the suitcase false bottom, using the materials — the outside checkered clothing, the bottom perimeter trough, the inside plastic casing, and the straps — from the second suitcase, to construct a two-inch-deep layer. He filled the false bottom with newspaper cut-out notes and concealed it with checkered cloth which later would be secured with straps, and on top of it, packed it with clothes, toiletries, and socks.

Next, he worked on the shoes. At first, he practiced on his old pair, prying out the second layer with the leather cutting knife, just as the cobbler had explained; then scooping out some holes in the heals to embed stones the size of the diamonds; and, finally, resoling it back with the glue, scrubbing all the excess glue oozing out from its edges.

Satisfied, he wrested the sole of his new shoes, and scooped out ten holes on each sole. The diamonds would be embedded and sealed the day of the departure.

Shaft paused and marveled at what he had done in the last five days. He was content with the work and called upon Walji to inspect the suitcase and the shoes in the secret workshop.

"I never realized you were so skillful," said Walji, and then added, "This is truly fantastic, very professional!"

"Good," said Shaft, beaming with pride and joy at Walji's approval.

"Can we reuse it for the next run?" asked Walji.

"May be the suitcase, not the shoes. The shoes will be discarded after delivery in Dubai. So I get to buy new shoes each trip," said Shaft amusingly.

"Well, I like the idea of walking around with $100,000.00 pair of shoes!" said Walji laughing.

After a time, Walji assumed his characteristically somber mood. He brushed his parted silky hair back with both his hands, and the smile on his face gave way to serious concern, his eyes narrowing and focusing on Shaft.

"We need to arrange a meeting with Joseph. Fill him in on the itinerary, pay him his advance, and then, we need to call Mr. Sharma and arrange for a meeting next week," Walji said.

They agreed to meet with Joseph on Monday, the week of departure. After work, Shaft would bring him straight to the room. Walji suggested that any signs of what transpired — Shaft's craftsmanship — over the last few days be purged. It was Walji's idea that going forward, all the encounters — meeting with people pertaining to the business — would be carried in this guest house room number 7. Walji would see to it that the room was never occupied. The renovation would be scheduled promptly, and this room number 7 would be transformed into Walji's office, with a phone and filing cabinets, and all the furnishings of a back office. This idea of the office — with secret dealings behind closed door upstairs in room number 7 of the guest house — gave it the glamour and drama of the clandestine world, accessible to only a select few shadowy figures, seamlessly flowing in and out of the restaurant into the secret chambers.

The next day, Walji contacted Mr. Sharma and gave him the departure date as previously discussed. They arranged to meet on Tuesday, the day before Shaft's departure, in the office. Mr. Sharma would have the gems, and together, they would visit Mr. Mohan Shah — a local jeweler nearby elected by Walji to vouch for the authenticity of the diamonds.

The week elapsed quickly; Monday came, and Shaft and Joseph knocked on the office door in the evening just after 7:00 PM as planned. Walji let them in.

The office was still in the making — the sofa and love seat replaced the bed, and a coffee table now stood in the center; along the back wall, next to entrance to the bathroom, an office desk without chairs was edged against the wall. On one side of the table was a black dial phone.

Walji sat on the love seat and gestured Shaft and Joseph towards the comfortable new sofa.

"Always good to see you, Joseph," beamed Walji.

After an exchange of pleasantries, Walji said, "Time has come, Joseph. Shaft will need your clearance on Wednesday."

"Yes, Shaft told me the details. I will be there personally. It is a good time — afternoon flight. And I will be there when he arrives. His safe return is part of my income," assured Joseph, hinting sublimely for the advance.

Walji picked up on the hint. He got up and went to the office desk. From one of the side drawers, he fished a brown, sealed envelope.

"It is all in there. The balance when Shaft returns. And you never know, there may be more," said Walji, catching Shaft's eye.

And then Walji returned back to the office desk, and from the drawer, he retrieved a bottle of whiskey and three shot glasses. He poured three shots and proposed a toast: "To new partnership, to new ventures. Cheers!"

After a few shots whisky and bantering, they settled for dinner downstairs. By now, Joseph was accustomed to Indian food and music, and everything that goes with it. He was comfortable around Shaft and Walji.

At one point during the dinner conversation, Joseph asked Walji how his mother was. Touched by his concern, Walji replied she was fine, but her health was declining. Later, Joseph asked Shaft if he could bring him some gifts: perfumes, fashionable shoes and purses from London. He said he wanted to give Miriam something for Christmas, something imported from London. Shaft obliged.

For Shaft and Walji, Joseph was an investment; he had to be kept content. The potential of his range of influence if he were promoted to senior management in customs controlling port entries into the country would be invaluable to future operations.

Soon, Joseph left. He took a taxi and used his first Sh100.00 note from the envelope. It felt good carrying wads of cash. A sense of euphoria and power engulfed him as he imagined the future wads of cash growing larger and the power it would endow him.

All guilt about loyalty to his civic duties purged. He knew Shaft was a courier for some local businessmen siphoning money out of the country. And he justified his transgression: if not him, someone in the office next door would be carrying this envelope home tonight. It was how things were now in the country. It was his way of trampling on the thorns of conscience pricking him. It was so easy, so effortless, so exuberant, this first step.

When he arrived at home, he dumped the cash on his bed, and realized that there were ten thousand shillings, instead of five. Was there a mistake? Perhaps the advance was a full payment — and more. Walji would not make such mistake; Indians do not make such mistakes with money — every penny is accounted for.

On Tuesday morning, Mr. Sharma gently knocked on the office door. This time, he did not stay at the guest house. He had traveled only for the meeting and had planned to depart soon after.

"Oh, Walji, *bhai*," how are you?" said Mr. Sharma, with his characteristic greeting, exposing his crimson-stained teeth from beetle juice.

Walji noticed he was less exuberant than before, his jauntiness dampened by apprehension. His eyes were narrow and shifty as he studied the room. He carried a small black leather briefcase that he kept close to himself.

He was entrusting Walji — half his age, brimming with apparent confidence — with a considerable fortune. But Mr. Sharma was no fool. He wanted assurance; should Walji abscond with the gemstones, he wanted him apprehended, and dealt with. So he hired a couple of Arab thugs from Tanga to shadow Walji all the time until the transaction was complete. They were to record and report to Mr. Sharma everyday Walji's movements – with whom he met and where, for how long, and how often.

"Have a seat," gestured Walji to the sofa, and Walji sat across from him on the love seat. On the coffee table lay some discarded Sunday newspaper and a couple of glossy magazines — *Stardust* and *Newsweek*, its cover story exposing American covert operations in Congo.

Walji waited for Mr. Sharma to initiate the rendezvous details. The silence got awkward. Finally, Walji spoke.

"The jeweler is not far from here. We should not keep him waiting. But before we go, we should talk about how my courier is going to deliver the goods, and how we want the commission delivered."

Mr. Sharma nodded.

"I am going to give you two phone numbers and a secret pass phrase. Your courier should call this number Thursday morning at 9:00 AM," Mr. Sharma said while extending a small piece of paper with two sets of numbers legibly scribbled on it.

"If no one answers, he should try again at 10:00 AM. The second number is only a backup if both times fail.

"Your courier should say to the person on the phone 'This is Hilton Hotel, Abu Dubai, Room Service. I have the broken glasses," and my contact will ask, "For what room number?" Your courier should reply, "Room number 20,"' explained Mr. Sharma.

"Elaborate protocol," said Walji, hiding his amusement and folly about this scheme of secret code phrases, the stuff of espionage novels and movies, then asked," Then what?"

"My contact will arrange an immediate meeting. He will provide the exact address of the jewelry shop and the name of the person to ask for. When he arrives at the shop, they will exchange the same phrase," said Mr. Sharma.

Walji took notes for Shaft. He reckoned Shaft would be exhilarated by the clandestine modes of communication — secret numbers, obscure phrases, and faceless voices on the phone in a foreign city.

Walji paused for a moment, looked up to Mr. Sharma, smiled, and put the writing pad on the coffee table. He realized that Mr. Sharma had all the details elaborately planned, all contingencies covered. He must have done this before countless times. Such intricate planning comes with experience. Walji curiously wondered why Mr. Sharma was turning towards him. Surely, he had other couriers do the run for him. Maybe, Walji speculated, there had been a betrayal or a run gone awry, and Walji was a safe bet.

It was Walji's turn to elaborate his end of the transaction. In his normal serious way, accentuating each syllable of the word, he explained.

"At the time when goods are delivered, I want you to be here with the money. Your contact and my courier should use the same phone from the same place to call us here in the office. After both confirm the goods delivered safely, our transaction is complete, and you hand me the money," explained Walji.

Mr. Sharma digested it for a moment. It was simple he thought.

"Okay," said Mr. Sharma.

"What about London?" asked Walji.

Mr. Sharma gave Walji a single London number. He instructed Walji to have his courier follow the same procedure. And Walji told him likewise, and gave Mr. Sharma the new office number. They both agreed on times and dates of delivery in Abu Dubai and London, and left the office for the jewelry shop.

The jeweler — a portly, bespectacled Indian man — welcomed them, and led them inside his office through an open doorway. He instructed his Indian assistant to order some tea. Walji declined the offer.

Through the large glass partition between the store and the office the shop appeared quiet, the street noise was silenced by the thick glass separation and the chatter of pedestrians and traffic on the street were muffled.

It was a typical jewelry store: glass show case and cabinets on both sides of the narrow store aisle displaying glittering gold and silver Indian-style jewelry: bangles, *bindis*, rings, ankle bracelets, diamond-tipped nose and finger rings.

The jeweler took his position behind a table. On the table was a contraption — a tripod with raised platform and a large, thick circular magnifying glass mounted on top. Underneath a tripod was a smooth, moveable velvet platform. Arching over the magnifying glass, an adjustable study lamp brightly illuminated the velvet platform.

Mr. Sharma placed his briefcase on the table, unlocked both small golden snap locks with a tiny key, and opened it. From it, he fished out a couple of blue velvet stringed bags, which he handed to the jeweler. The jeweler diligently emptied the contents of each bag on a glass tray; the luminous sparkling diamonds clattered against its smooth surface.

Twenty pieces — all clear, transparent with the iridescent light from the lamp reflecting and refracting from its round cuts: the sheer brilliance exhilarated Walji. He had never seen real diamonds before; Tanzanite, which is a deep turquoise gemstone, is no match in its sparkle.

The jeweler picked up each piece with a pair of tweezers and placed it on a small scale, weighing them each separately and jotting each measurement. One at a time, he picked each diamond, placed it on the velvet platform, raised the platform closer to the glass, and peered through it, nudging the gemstones at various angles.

Satisfied, the jeweler turned off the lamp, placed the diamonds back into the stringed bag, and handed them to Mr. Sharma, who swiftly stashed it away into the briefcase.

"They all are 1.5 carat, genuine, round cut, no stains or damage. Good stones. They are not from around here. Most probably Angola or South Africa," declared the jeweler.

Mr. Sharma remained silent all along, satisfied. He was content to put Walji's doubt about the authenticity of the gemstones to rest, but at the same time, he had to ensure Walji delivered the entrusted merchandise. Betrayal, he told himself this time, would have dire consequences.

Walji expressed his gratitude to the jeweler and asked for some smooth velvet cloth. The jeweler went to one of the lined cabinets and retrieved a square piece of velvet cloth used to encase and protect gemstones. Then he picked up a small receipt book, placed a carbon copy underneath its first page, and scribbled his service charges on it. He tore the page and handed it to Walji, who paid him the full amount.

Inside the shop, buzzing fans cooled them; outside, the heat from the street pavement seared them as they walked across the street towards the restaurant. The tea Mr. Sharma drank at the jeweler's shop made him sweat profusely as he walked.

Upstairs in the office, Mr. Sharma handed the two bags to Walji, and said primly, "I entrust you with this. Please make sure it gets delivered."

Before Mr. Sharma left, he told Walji that next time when they meet they all will be compensated with their cuts as middlemen. Walji's somber expression gave way to a hearty chuckle.

Outside on the street, Mr. Sharma's eyes caught the glaring stare of his two hired thugs — lazily leaning against the wall across the street — as he emerged from the alley alongside the restaurant in the bright light of the afternoon. He nodded at them, and hailed for a taxi, which swiftly came to the curb side. His nod signaled the burly thugs to shadow Walji's every move, and inform Mr. Sharma every day by phone.

In the evening, the night before departure, Shaft and Walji met upstairs in the office. Shaft had packed an old suitcase with his traveling clothes. He had told his parents he had to take a business trip for the immigration office. At work, he had taken two weeks leave. It wasn't easy to ask for leave on short notice — vacations were planned ahead — but he managed to convince his department head, with help from Mr. Kibala.

Shaft fetched the false-bottom suitcase from the office cupboard where Walji had kept it, along with the platform shoes. Walji gave him the 10,000.00 dollars – all tightly compacted and wrapped in ten one-thousand dollar stacks.

Then he gave him another $10,000.00 dollars. Shaft looked surprised.

"Mr. Lakhani wants this delivered to the named contact in London. The details are in the envelope. Don't worry; the cut is the same for us," Walji said, smiling.

Shaft laid all the stacks on the bottom, covered with a thin plastic film. It didn't occupy much of the false bottom; it could easily hold $100,000.00 if tightly compacted.

Shaft carefully secured the straps and the extra cloth lining he had ripped from the second identical suitcase and glued it on top, making it appear as part of the bottom. He then laid all his clothes on top, some carefully folded; others rumpled as if the suitcase was hurriedly packed.

Satisfied, he turned to Walji for approval, who gleefully nodded, and went to his desk to retrieve the diamonds.

Walji tilted the empty bags into his hands, and the glittering stone's light danced off the room's evening light. Shaft marveled at its sparkling beauty. He looked on and held it in his palm, admiring its sheer brilliance.

"That is our future fortune, my friend," said Walji smugly.

"Beautiful! Now I understand why rich women love diamonds," said Shaft ponderously.

"We have to be careful not to stain them. I have extra velvet cloth. I want you to cut small pieces and wrap each of them before you embed them into your shoes," said Walji, concerned.

Together, they cut up twenty small pieces of velvet and carefully wrapped each stone — like a newly-born baby. Using his thumb, Shaft embedded each purple velvet ball deep into the gorged cavity of his new platform sole, and pushed with his index finger until it snugly fitted. He then covered both soles with a thin layer of plastic film, applied the leather glue and attached the sole to it, wiping off any extra glue emitting from its rims.

Shaft applied constant pressure to each sole for some time till both soles were attached. He held them up to Walji, who gave him a look of contentment.

"My $100,000.00 dollars shoes, man!" exclaimed Shaft.

They laughed with an air of premature jubilation.

"Ah, you will enjoy this, Shaft." Walji said, recalling Mr. Sharma's elaborate protocol.

He reached for his notepad and discussed with Shaft the elaborate rendezvous details. Shaft listened intently, his moustache twitching above his lips, visualizing it all: the telephone booth on some street corner or hotel lobby; the faceless voice on the phone; the meeting place, just like in the movies. It accentuated the excitement and drama on the eve of his first-ever run. Yet he remained calm.

Walji urged Shaft to memorize the numbers and the phrases in case he lost the paper. Both went over the details one more time before Shaft placed the paper in his jacket.

"Are you coming to the airport?" asked Shaft.

"Yes, this first time. I want to make sure all is well. Joseph said he will to be there, but I want to be sure," said Walji.

Shaft nodded, and gestured for some drinks. It was still hot and humid outside, the air still. Even though the sun had gone down, the African sky still had its fading orange glow, with mile-long bands of gray cloud in the foreground.

Walji hailed the taxi and Osman took them to the Rex Hotel in town. Behind them, the two burly thugs hailed the second taxi, and shadowed them.

Shaft lay in bed, restless, staring at the white ceiling, imagining Dubai, but failed any further than what he had seen in the embassy brochures. His goal, he convinced himself, was to deliver the goods, and receive his profitable cut upon his return; that was all that mattered to him. Yet he entertained a deceitful idea, and dismissed it straightway, focusing on the tasks of the journey never taken before.

He knew he would have to rely on his street smarts and that his instinct would guide him. *People are the same everywhere*, he thought; *they have the same weaknesses.*

His mind drifted aimlessly for the next hour, then his eyelids got heavy, and within minutes, he slipped into deep slumber. The night gave way to bright light outside. The street was busy as usual at this hour of the day; it was not until 10:00 AM that Shaft woke.

Walji was in the office when Shaft arrived with his toiletry bag. They had breakfast brought to them in the office from the restaurant. Shaft picked up his platform shoes and studied them carefully, looking for any signs of obvious clues. Walji waited for any signs of concern, but Shaft assuredly said "No problem," after examining his "fortune" shoes.

After a time, Shaft put on the "fortune" shoes and carried his suitcase downstairs. Walji had arranged for Osman to take them to the airport at 12:00 noon. Osman pulled up outside the restaurant and Walji and Shaft boarded the taxi; behind them, another taxi pulled over, and Mr. Sharma's shadow figures jumped into it, and instructed the driver to follow the car ahead of them.

The drive to the airport was over a few miles of potholed tarmac road outside Dar, past the industrial area, past the shanty towns and the makeshift kiosks selling fruits and bottled drinks. Suddenly — through an open area of uncultivated vegetation on either side of the road with stretches of thorny shrubbery and wild brush — they emerged towards a two-story glass building with the traffic controller tower emerging from the left end of the building, its twirling radar on the top.

Jet fuel fumes from the recent flights lingered in the humid, dense, afternoon air. It was a dull afternoon at the airport. The busiest times were weekends, when the European international carriers arrived and departed; weekdays were consigned for domestic flights, and the less-glamorous carriers that flew within the continent.

Porters lumbered around the metal railings leading to the entrance, waiting to be summoned. Shaft and Walji went past the railings into the departure checking area. A few people were gathered in groups, mostly families present to bid farewell.

A queue had formed at the Air Tanzania counter. A young, attractive African woman — in a smart uniform: light blue shirt, dark blue skirt, national flag-colored scarf loosely wrapped around her slender neck, and a tilted hat, secured at each end with hair clips – with a friendly disposition attended to each passenger. When Shaft gave her his ticket and passport, she asked him if he wanted a window or an aisle seat.

"Window, please," Shaft said.

He said he wanted to see the departing and arriving cities below him – at night, as well as day.

"You will be arriving late evening, after sunset. Abu Dubai has glittering lights," the ticket attendant said, smiling.

The ticket clerk then directed Shaft to the immigration and customs for baggage checking, which was to the end of the ticket counter: a low, wooden deck on which travelers placed their luggage for inspection. On the opposite side of the wooden deck, two African customs officials with scowling frowns rudely commanded the passengers to open their bags, and roughly searched the suitcases, turning each layer of neatly arranged clothes.

As Shaft arrived at the deck, Joseph emerged, in his official uniform, from a glass office at the end of the hall. He looked grave as he approached Shaft.

Joseph directed his two junior officers to attend an Arab couple while he attended to Shaft. Joseph perfunctorily asked Shaft questions; Shaft answered with a straight face. Then, Joseph took his white piece of chalk and marked Shaft's bag. He signaled the porter to place it along with other inspected baggage on the conveyer belt.

From behind a rope-partitioned area, Walji anxiously observed, leaning against a pillar. And behind him, unaware of them, lurking amongst the departing families, were Mr. Sharma's heavies. They knew who the courier was, and soon so would Mr. Sharma, but he was less interested in the courier; his focus was Walji. Mr. Sharma knew that through Walji he could — if need arises — reach the courier.

Departing lounges are solemn places, full of sad faces, some envious, especially the young ones, dreaming of their escape from the dreadful clutches of boredom and stagnancy in the country. Today, most passengers on that plane to Dubai were Asians and Arabs, most leaving for good. Shaft and a couple of other were the only African-looking passengers.

When Walji caught Shaft's eye, he summoned him towards the rope.

"As soon as you arrive and get to the hotel, call the office. I will be there late tonight," Walji insisted.

Shaft gave Walji a nervous smile, an averted look as if his eyes would reveal what he was thinking all along, and said, "Sure," and walked away from Walji, straight through the narrow hallway into the departing lounge, away from the crowd, conscious of Walji's inquiring eyes following him. Shaft never turned and looked back.

Walji had sensed a change in Shaft's demeanor, but he attributed it to anxiety. After all, this was his first airplane trip abroad, he told himself; what lies ahead is an encounter with Dubai customs, followed by London. There is no Joseph there to wave him through; he would have to rely on his calm and confidence and wit.

All this time Walji never imagined whether Shaft would abscond and betray him. Why would he? There was so much more ahead for both; this run was only the beginning, only a trial run to establish ground work for subsequent ones. But after that look in Shaft's eyes — the downcast eyes of guilt — the specter of betrayal suddenly raised in Walji's mind. As often as he tried to dismiss it, as often as he tried to justify it — that it was nothing but Shaft's travel anxiety

— doubt and worry consumed him on his ride back to the restaurant — and for the rest of the evening.

That evening, Walji confined himself to the room with a bottle of whiskey, awaiting a phone call from Shaft. The phone never rang. A whole day went by without the office phone ringing.

Perhaps, Walji thought to console himself, Shaft was caught smuggling and held by the authorities at the airport, but how would Walji know of such news. Mr. Sharma was due the next day according to plan, and by then, Shaft should have made rendezvous with the Dubai contact, and all involved parties posed to exchange the merchandize and receive their respective cuts.

Every minute of the next twenty-four hours was dreadful for Walji. He had not slept for the last day and half. He was coming around to accept two possibilities: Shaft betrayed him, or Shaft was apprehended at the Dubai airport. Neither could be verified. He assembled enough thoughts, a story line, to face Mr. Sharma who was due any minute.

A soft knock on the door startled him. Walji let Mr. Sharma in.

"Ah *bhai*, how are you?" said Mr. Sharma softly, raising his briefcase to suggest to Walji that he had the money for him, and set on the sofa, placing the briefcase beside him. Walji recognized the briefcase from the previous meeting – then it carried diamonds; now, perhaps, money or a concealed weapon to snuff him, Walji imagined.

Mr. Sharma seemed agitated and concerned as he faced Walji, who leaned against the office desk edge close to the rotary dial phone.

"Your courier has failed to make rendezvous. Today was the day! Has he made contact with you?" asked Mr. Sharma angrily.

"No. But there was a phone call very late last night. I was not sure if I was dreaming. I think we should give him time. Something unexpected might have happened. He has four days in Dubai. I am sure any one of these days, the phone will ring," Walji said, gathering his confidence amidst apprehension and the realization of naked truth of what might have really happened.

"I don't have four days to wait here with you next to the phone!" screamed Mr. Sharma.

Walji walked behind the table and pulled out a couple of shot glasses and poured a stiff drink for both of them, and handed one to Mr. Sharma, who gulped it down, and asked for more.

Awkward silence weighed on them like tons of brick. No small talk would mitigate the anxiety that filled the air in the small office. Walji opened the door to let some fresh air in, and stood by the doorway, looking away, glass in hand, awaiting rescue from that black contraption behind him on the table; its musical ring was his lifeline. And only Shaft, his partner in crime and his mate, could play that tune.

But it was never to be.

Mr. Sharma, red-faced as rage consumed him, continued to drink from the bottle left on the coffee table, as both middlemen awaited, burdened by their underground world of mistrust and deceit and betrayal.

At last, Mr. Sharma got up and menacingly told Walji he better pray for his life for the next two days. Walji saw a perilous side of the portly, *pan*-eating man.

"Don't worry; it will come through," Walji said comfortingly, searching for words of assurance.

"I have been in this business long enough to know the signs," said Mr. Sharma, mockingly, his face close to Walji.

Walji offered Mr. Sharma a room to stay in while they both anxiously waited in separate rooms.

Even as Walji acted, putting up a brave face for the next two days — comforting Mr. Sharma, convincing him that perhaps his courier was apprehended by the Dubai authorities — he knew his adversary was no fool. Mr. Sharma had his theories: he had been had for the second time. The wrath of a duped man in the underground world cannot be underestimated.

Thursday and Friday passed in silence, the phone in the office never rang. At the end of Friday evening, the raging Mr. Sharma told Walji he would make some phone calls to his contact in Dubai, and stormed out.

Walji was relieved when Mr. Sharma departed with his briefcase, but an ominous sense of danger engulfed Walji; he feared for his life. A week elapsed, waiting in harrowing silence: no news from Mr. Sharma — or Shaft.

Consumed with uncertainty — and the realization of betrayal – Walji was depressed, and took to heavy drinking at nights. The following Saturday night, after a round of heavy drinking at the New Africa Hotel, on his way home, slightly drunk, Walji hailed a taxi driven by one of Mr. Sharma's heavies. The Arab thug drove the taxi for a short distance along Samora Michel Avenue before stopping to pick up his burly companion.

Six months later, a decapitated and badly-decomposed body of an Asian man washed ashore in a small fishing village in Tanga. It was never identified as that of Walji. There were no dental records or DNA samples to match. It lay in the government morgue in Tanga for weeks, unclaimed, until finally, it was incinerated.

Mr. Sharma had his revenge, but he could never find out — even while torturing Walji during his captivity with help of the two burly thugs — what had happened of Shaft. He had simply disappeared. Mr. Sharma was betrayed for the second time, and relinquished the idea of sending the two thugs after Shaft; it was futile as he could be anywhere in the world.

Rumors spread in the community and at the mosque down the street from the restaurant that Walji and Shaft had absconded with large sums of money. Mr. Lakhani, who lost his US $10,000.00, was eager to point out his loss. Many believed the story; many had suspected their wheeling and dealing: how else could they be supporting their flamboyant lifestyle over the past year with meager clerk's wages?

Walji's ailing mother died within a few weeks of her son's disappearance; the taunts at the mosque were unbearable and it killed her like slow poison; and Shaft's parents, disgraced by their adopted son's scandal, returned to the interior, away from the nauseating communal verbal rebuke.

Over time (more than a decade), Walji and Shaft's misdeeds were purged and eventually faded away by other changes around the country. A new spirit had emerged and embraced the people: there was talk about liberalizing the economy; there was talk about *Mwalimu* willingly stepping down as the president — something no other African leader had done before.

Businesses, once nationalized, were returned back to their proprietary Asian owners, who started all over again, their resilience and merchant spirit rekindled in the new free-market economic policies gradually introduced by the government after dismal failures of a long decade of socialist policies.

Up north, in neighboring Uganda, Idi Amin had fled to Saudi Arabia and the new government of exiled Milton Obote was followed by Museveni, who immediately embraced free-market economic policies to revive his ravaged country from civil war; down south, liberation armies reveled in symbolic victories over the colonial powers. Financial aid from the first world flowed in, like water from an open faucet, all to support the new hopeful mood of the country.

Businesses around town and trade to and from neighboring countries began to flourish, and the snuffed entrepreneurial flame of the early years was reignited. All signs of economic boom — and a new life — were in the making: there were no more empty shelves in stores and the supermarkets. Those with the means enjoyed the consumer luxury.

Africans, especially from the northern part of the country, competed with their Asian counterparts, and controlled much of the northern towns' retail commerce, just as Asians once did. Upcountry Africans were climbing their ladders of social and economic mobility.

Joseph was promoted to senior management and was now in charge of port authorities along coastal cities of Dar, Tanga, Bagamoyo, and Mafia. With the promotion, came a house in the posh Msasani neighborhood. His tenable and influential post attracted wealthy Asian businessmen's interest, especially those involved in container shipments of goods for import and export.

With hefty kickbacks, he amassed large sums of money and lived the life of luxury. Miriam was just another of his weekend concubine — and she enjoyed Joseph, whenever possible, as much as she relished her other wealthy clients.

Money and power corrupted Joseph. His early middlemen, no longer with him, had paved the road for him, and ever since that first payment — in a small room above an Indian restaurant in town — he had no regrets. He and Miriam often wondered (and talked about) what had happened to Shaft and Walji; they could only speculate.

A community member, returning from London, had recognized Shaft — flanked by a couple of blondes, outside their South Kensington mosque one Friday after evening prayers. He was eating some Indian snacks at the corner shop, owned by one of the recent Asian immigrants from Tanzania — in London. Theirs was a cliquish community; people knew of new arrivals in the newly-adopted land. The mosque in London, just as the one at home, was their center of their social life in the newly-adopted land: it comforted them, provided a sense of community, eased with the transition, and furnished the strength to cope with the harsh realities of the new world.

It was the last time anybody heard of Shaft. London had become Shaft's sanctuary; its world of peoples of African descent (West Indians) in neighborhoods such as Brixton, Notting Hill, and Hackney — offered him anonymity. He had enough money to last him a long time.

He never regretted betraying Walji. While in the departing lounge at the Dar airport (and shortly before his departure), he had contemplated flight and betrayal. And the moment he stepped on the tarmac, walking towards the plane on the hangar, Shaft never looked back; he closed all doors to his previous life, purging everybody who was part of it.

The Marxist and His Sister

Part I

From his early years in life, Sadruddin Kassam — or Sadru, as his sister Roshan called him — remained attached to an idea only fleetingly, like a social fad, and would then move onto the next big thing that came his way. This pattern of seamless scurrying through the revolving doors of society from his formative years continued into his adult life.

Now in his late twenties, when Sadru embraces an idea, his self-absorption is rapturous; for him, each revelation, each exposure to a novel idea is a moment of repeated epiphany.

With the emphatic passion and zealotry of a newly converted, he would proclaim to his friends:

"Weh, *bana*, my life has changed, man!"

How they would inquire?

Sadru would then parrot vacuous sermons, often verbatim, from pamphlets, books and foreign magazines he had read. His natural gift to memorize passages of text from books gave him the credence of an erudite person. In his readings, he would underline passages of text that seem eloquent, and he would incorporate them in his daily speech, giving him a sense of a "man of the books," for others around him looked up to him as such.

To complete a self-cultivated intellectual image, Sadru donned a white pressed shirt and khaki or dark trousers and beige suede shoes, an image typical of a government secondary school teacher. He combed back his wavy, black hair, held together with Yardley gel, accentuating his forehead.

He knew that with his hair tightly held back and a thick, black-framed glasses on his narrow face sporting a scruffy goatee gave him an uncanny resemblance to the South African exiled poet Dennis Brutus, who presently was lecturing at the University of Dar es Salaam, the "Hill", where the poet had acquired a celebrity status — a literary weapon against the indomitable apartheid regime of South Africa.

Often, students of African poetry at the Hill familiar with Dennis Brutus noticed the resemblance and they would compliment Sadru; on more than one occasion, an African student girl at the Hill approached Sadru, mistaking him for the famed poet. These incidents stroked Sadru's ego, but his modesty belied his craving for these compliments.

It was at the Hill that Sadru made his first acquaintance with a circle of fellow Asian compatriots — students and academics and professionals — who turned him onto revolutionary leftist ideology. Later on, he was invited to attend weekend seminars and discussion groups.

Such gatherings were normally held at a lecturer's residence on the scenic part of the Hill: smallish bungalows on manicured lawns and resplendent bougainvillea sprawling over fences overlooking the campus. Invariably, these meetings were charged and spirited by local and exiled academics, the likes of Walter Rodney, and occasionally, by members of the African National Congress, whose headquarters were based in Dar es Salaam. Sometimes, upon invitation, personnel attached to the Cuban and Russian embassies for cultural affairs would make special appearances as dignitaries extolling the glorious virtues of socialism in their respective countries. From time to time, local academics would discuss the dialectics of Marxist ideology. The Hill at the time was the pinnacle of African *zeitgeis*t. Leftist academics from Europe eager to proselytize their interpretation of the works of Marx, Hegel, Engel, Herzen, Lenin, and Mao flocked willingly to the African plains as visiting professors.

And Sadru relished the atmosphere and was enamored by these cliquish weekly rendezvous. From it, he derived an inflated sense of self-importance and hubris by association with the fledging leftist intelligentsia; he acquired loathsome superiority with which he frowned upon his sheltered Asian brethren in his community — many of whom were shopkeepers, *duka-wallas*, traders, wheelers-and-dealers, small scale industrialists and property owners — who were shrewd in their predatory business practices, controlling much of the service market economy in the country. In Sadru's borrowed parlance, which he spewed now and then when among the less-read, they were the "capitalist pigs," the "Jews of Africa," and *uyonyanjis* (blood suckers).

Every Sunday morning, without failure, Sadru would drive his sister Roshan's car to the Hill. Over time, he abandoned driving the car and, instead, elected to ride the local bus to the Hill from a bus stop just a short walk from his sister's flat off Upanga Road, to attend the discussion groups.

One Sunday morning, he did not show up for breakfast at Roshan's flat to pick up the car. Instead, he walked from his flat on Aly Khan Road, past the inescapable and dominant two-story clock-towered mosque, with arched glass windows, to the bus stop.

The next day, when Sadru stopped by at Roshan's flat, she asked, "What happened? You overslept? Had a bit too much to drink at Palm Beach Hotel Saturday night?"

"No. I took the bus."

"Bus? I lived here forty years, and I have never taken a bus or even seen the inside of the bus. Each time it goes by here, man, it is packed inside. Everybody is sweating in this heat. *Bapa*, not me, never, eh!"

Roshan refrained from the usage of the casual derogatory word to refer to Africans. She had grown conscious that Sadru was annoyed when she employed it.

Sadru thought perhaps he should explain why he took the bus but instead dismissed the idea. It would be futile, he concluded. She would not comprehend the world he was entering and embracing so starkly in conflict to her privileged one.

Instead he said, "It is Sunday, Roshan. The buses are quite empty in the morning. That way, you can use the car. I just park it there for the entire day."

But his riding the bus was a gesture of political statement, a renouncement of his accessibility to luxury and privilege. The conflict was apparent, and it consumed him. He began to internalize the socialist ideals. He yearned to be part of the struggling proletariat and wanted to be connected to the African downtrodden workers who rode buses, day-in-day-out, to and from the townships of their mud and cement dwellings at the outskirts of the city. He wanted a sense of belonging, to be part of the larger society than his limited one.

"I meant to ask you," Roshan hesitated and then braved, "You have been going to the Hill every Sunday. Are you seeing someone?"

"Oh no!" replied Sadru, avoiding her intrusive sisterly gaze, "I just attend some Sunday study sessions," replied Sadru, breaking eye contact with her.

Roshan did not probe any further. She sensed from his averted look that he did not wish to elaborate. She was fond of his brother and drew a line beyond which she would not forage into his personal life. Yet, sometimes she could not suppress her maternal sentiments, especially after both their parents had died of mysterious illness, when Sadru was only thirteen; she had shouldered the burden of providing for him.

Sadru had been attending the weekend meetings for the past six months, but he never revealed to Roshan about its true nature, never discussed about it.

A couple of years ago, after Sadru completed a two-year teachers training program at a college in Morogoro in 1970, Roshan had urged him to join the family scrap metal business, but he had gracefully brushed aside the idea. He said he was unsure what he wanted to do – whether continue a graduate degree in education or attempt some teaching first or embrace the next the "big thing" that captivated him.

Sadru's decision to attend teacher's training program did not stem from personal conviction that the pursuit of teaching and propagating knowledge is a worthy profession and a noble cause, but was influenced by the glamour of the character, its portrayed idealism, played by Sidney Poitier in

To Sir with Love. And so, he enrolled at the teachers college in Morogoro.

A month later that year, Roshan's husband, Noordin, died of a massive stroke and left behind a fortune and a lucrative business of exporting scrap metal to England. She was devastated and desperately needed Sadru's support, at least initially, until her two children finished their university education in England to take over the business.

Noordin had taught Roshan all the intricacies of the business; and Roshan, compared to other Asian women in her community, was fiercely independent and shrewd. She could have easily run the operation alone, but Sadru obliged, perhaps out of guilt, even if it was only for a short duration, and joined Roshan to manage the enterprise until his nephews returned within a year of completing their courses.

At the time, he felt he could not see his sister suffer in isolation, could not abandon her in her moment of need. After what Noordin and Roshan had provided for him and their ailing parents, his family loyalty, obligation, and burden triumphed over his personal ambitions.

But what were Sadru's ambitions? They changed like seasons.

Since Noordin's death, Sadru was by Roshan's side in business, engaged in profiteering, for over a year; but then on weekends, through his associations with leftist intelligentsia, he was undergoing a personal transformation: he was embracing the Marxist notions of social and monetary equity of the proletariats; he was sympathizing with the oppressed, condemning the ruling class; he was shouldering the burden of collective guilt for being an Asian, for belonging to the merchant class, without any perspective of his historic past, or the struggles of his forefathers who came to Africa from

India, some as indentured workers, others as penniless traders, to build a future for their progeny.

Sadru was riding the political wave at its peak, sweeping the continent from Algeria in the north to South Africa in the south, all countries under transformation from the colonial past — some still engulfed in a bitter armed struggle for their freedom.

It was just a matter of time before Sadru's newly embraced ideals would undermine his loyalties to the commercial motives of his sister's enterprise.

Every day, Sadru and Roshan drove to work, with Roshan driving in the morning in their gray Peugeot 504, and Sadru driving back in the evening, a ritual observed ever since that first day when Roshan returned back to work twelve weeks after Noordin's funeral. She had confided in Sadru one evening on their drive back home from the cemetery, after her forty-day ritual of mourning.

"I can't stay at home all day. I will go mad. I need my routine," Roshan pleaded, looking out the window at a line of elegant colonial bungalows owned by Europeans along both sides of the Oyster Bay Road, their manicured lawns tended by African gardeners dressed in starch-white washed uniforms.

"Aren't you supposed to mourn for few a months?"

"Yes, forty days, if you follow traditions. And forty days are over. Both Al-Karim and Yasmin are going back to London this week. I will be alone at home. I will go mad!" cried Roshan.

The early weeks after Noordin's death were wretched for Roshan; she had aged, the dark shadows under her eyes had deepened, and the lines of age had marked her face. During these days of mourning, Sadru spent the nights at her house, and late into the night, he heard her muffled sobs of sorrow and loss. Yet she remained strong, in front of her two London-returned children who were there briefly for their dad's funeral, and upon her insistence returned soon to finish their course. What carried her through the emptiness that follows the loss of a spouse was her unwavering conviction in the comfort and soothing effects of her prayers and her faith, and the rituals at the Upanga mosque.

%

The Kassam Scrap Metal Exporters, Ltd. was a typical rectangular compound with twelve-foot-high gray concrete walls, mildewed from moisture and humidity. Along the top of each wall were shards of embedded colored, broken glass, used as a deterrent for nocturnal visitors climbing over it. The front wall facing the dirt road parted in the middle with a wide iron-crossed gate that provided the only entrance to the compound. The gate was manned, day and night, by an African watchman during the day, and at night by another watchman with a fierce Alsatian dog.

To one side of the compound was the main rectangular office building with three small rooms, each with barred windows, and a pyramid shaped corrugated roof; the other side housed a large open barn area under a tin roof where the bulk of the scrap metal was hoarded before being carried off for export; and to the far side was the workers' area: a small shack for toilet and a wooden table and bench under a leaky, rusted, tin roof.

The compound was near the industrial area of the city, dotted with small scale factories, auto-garages, breweries and tanneries, all accessible via dirt roads off the main tarmac road leading to Dar's only airport.

Not far from this industrial area was the burgeoning African township of Magomeni with open sewages, mosquito-infested water puddles, and brick-walled low dwellings without basic amenities. Its inhabitants furnished the labor during the day and equal share of gruesome crime at night. On warm summer nights, the fecund stench from its open sewage lingered in the air. Drunkards, petty thieves, prostitutes, workers, and children, all lived in this cesspool of humanity, invisible to outsiders.

On each Friday of the last month, all day long, the compound is deluged with the steady traffic of lorries and small pick-up trucks bearing loads of scrap metal to be off-loaded by the compound workers, weighed and dumped in the barn, where at a later date, it would be hauled away for shipment.

Sadru diligently directed and coordinated this effort. For each weighted load, Sadru would write a note of its weight and amount on a small writing pad with the company's title on its page and hand it to the bearer. The note bearer would then walk across the open compound to the building office to hand the prescription to Roshan. She would disappear in the next room to retrieve the mutually agreed upon amount from the walled safe while the note bearer patiently waited for his small fortune, seated on an upholstered sofa under a ceiling fan, across from Roshan's paper littered table.

A truck load of non-rusted scrap metal, about 500 to 1000 kilograms, could fetch a couple of thousand shillings.

Before handing the cash, Roshan would ask the note bearer:

"How much should I write the receipt for? It says 300 kilos here."

"Make it for 200 kilos," the note bearer would suggest.

"How about 150 kilos," Roshan would insist.

"Okay," the note bearer would agree.

And this deceitful dialogue went on all day long with each scrap metal seller. All transactions were carried in cash. It was a deliberate scheme to avoid declaring real profits, and circumspect incurring large business taxes. With no track record, no audit trail for tax purposes, both the seller and buyer, at will, could fudge the real transactions and hide the real profits from the government. Such unaccountable and tax-evasive business practices and the culture of impunity were not uncommon: it was pervasive and rampantly growing, permeating all facets of society; it was robbing the country from one of its sources of income: taxes.

But it had its share of risks: like the anxiety Roshan and Noordin had to endure carrying large amounts of cash in the car to the compound once a month from the bank in town, or the fear of being discovered and reprimanded with an enormous tax penalty, and even worse, a court order for closure of the business. Perhaps the profits were so much better, lucrative, even if so much else was worse.

So far nothing dramatic had happened; this once-a-month business ritualistic operation had gone smoothly, unhindered and uninterrupted by any criminal incidents. All the profits garnered, deposited directly to the foreign account in London by the importers, were worth the risk for the future financial safety net it provided for Roshan and her children studying abroad.

Over the weeks, Roshan observed a gradual transformation in Sadru's social demeanor towards the compound African workers. She noted he was less commanding, less authoritarian, and exhibited a level of equality towards them. She feared that such casual relationship between the worker and the boss may undermine the productivity. She recalled Noordin was always firm with all the workers, though he paid them well — beyond what the minimal wage was — but in return, he commanded loyalty and hard work. But Sadru was nowhere close to what Noordin was.

Sometimes at lunch break, instead of eating with Roshan in one of the office rooms converted into a small kitchen, Sadru lunched with the workers outside in the compound, sharing his loaf of bread, chapatti, and curry, laughing and rejoicing the results of a football game from the weekend before, or talking about an incident reported in the Kiswahili newspaper, *Ngurumo*.

At first, Sadru was met with an awkward, silent rejection as he approached a small group of his employees and asked if he could sit and have lunch with them. The workers looked at him, surprised, and out of respect, cleared the bench, and gestured him to sit down. Normally, business owners did not do that; they had their own comfortable area for lunch and respite; the social boundaries were well defined and marked and mutually known: segregated.

But for Sadru, those distinctions of class and privilege contrasted with everything he had absorbed and internalized from his weekend socialist learning, from leftist literature he had read about workers' power, their role in the socialist national economy, and its equitable returns, and their control over the means of production. Such desire for a personal bond with the oppressed was his validation of his embraced ideals and beliefs. Just as taking a bus, instead of driving Roshan's car, gave him the proximity to masses, so did eating and palavering with the compound workers.

He went further in his gestures of solidarity. As a self-proclaimed Marxist, Sadru justified aiding the African clients who came to sell scrap metal by the cart-wheels —

the ones who would roam shirtless in the African searing heat to the deserted junk yards of Magomeni and extract discarded metal from piles of rotting rubbish — by falsely doubling the weight and recording it on the promissory note for Roshan, which would earn twice as much for the actual weight. This act of connivance pleased him in more ways than one; it gave him a convoluted sense of equity, as if it negated and purged any other improbity conducted by Roshan, and others like her.

One evening, on the way home while Sadru drove, just after they left the potholed dirt roads of the industrial area and before entering the main tarmac road from the airport leading into town, Roshan broached the subject of what she had observed days before. She waited for the opportune moment to confront Sadru.

From early years after their mother had died and she had taken Sadru into her wings, she had developed an ability to penetrate into his mind and read these sudden acts of passion. She sensed that these sudden acts of equality had its source elsewhere. And she wanted to get rid of them; they were, she thought, detrimental to the business climate.

"Sadru," Roshan said somberly, "You have worked here for over a year now. You are getting paid well. You are to the business what Noordin was. You are the manager. But this eating and drinking with workers every day worries me."

Sadru focused on the road ahead. A bus in front of him tilted slightly to the left from its human cargo, packed with African riders, a few hanging by the door at the end of the bus, all going home to their shanty dwellings in this area or to another township in a different part of the city.

I am not what Noordin was Sadru thought of rebutting, but refrained. Noordin owned and built this place; he made a fortune, while I am just earning a temporary salary to help you until your two children return from the prestigious colleges from overseas and so you all can continue sucking wealth out of the country: *sucking wealth out of the country*. It was a borrowed phrase with painful grains of truth.

Instead, he fell back on his skill and ability to extract information at will. He recalled an American visiting lecturer at the teacher's training college who extolled on the virtues of establishing good rapport with your students as an effective means of teaching.

Sadru said, without looking at Roshan, still focused on the bulging bus ahead of him, "Sometimes it helps if students are not scared of you and can talk freely with you."

"But they are not students. They work for us!" Roshan cried, the subtlety escaping Roshan, unable to disguise her irritation.

"There is an advantage when your workers are at ease with you," Sadru continued. "It builds trust."

"Trust? my foot! They will take advantage of you. They will ask for extra days off or want more money, or something or the other. I know their lot. You have to be firm with the workers. No slacking off. This is a business that requires work and discipline. We cannot afford slacking," she lamented.

Traffic in the evening on the only two-way tarmac road connecting the city center and the industrial area along the outskirts of Magomeni limped along, paraded with pedestrians, on either side of the road, darting and meandering between cars to cross the road; cyclists, sometimes carrying another passenger seated on the back seat or on the bar connected to the handles, clinked their bells with their thumb fingers, alerting their presence. Cars honked, adding to the cacophony of noise. Overcrowded yellow and white buses emitted their exhaust fumes as they made frequent stops, loading and unloading their human cargo.

The luminous African sky with endless rows of cirrus clouds marked the ending of the day. On the far left side of the road in the open space of dirt, ragged-clothed African youngsters played football with bare feet on a dirt pitch marked by two stones on each end as goal posts; it was a common sight along this long stretch of tarmac road dotted with make-shift dwellings and rickety stalls selling fruits, dried fish, and bottled juices.

This was the world of the oppressed, Sadru saw with his new Marxist lenses as he drove past them, a stark reminder to an outsider of the disparity between the haves and the have-nots, while for Roshan it was all invisible — something there, distant and unknown, left alone to survive its thrifty existence, so long as it provided the labor to drive the perpetual engines of commerce.

"I can still be firm and yet have lunch, talk about things with them. I don't see anything wrong with that," explained Sadru, disguising his irritability at her sister's entrenched beliefs and notions of African workers.

"Yes, I don't see anything wrong in talking. I do that too once in a while. Ask them about their families. Noordin did that all the time. Noordin even paid expenses when Osman had to travel to Shinyanga for his father's funeral. When Baraka's son died, Noordin went to the funeral, he paid wages for three months while Baraka grieved. It is not like we treat them as slaves. Tell me how many others do that?" asked, Roshan.

"But I think," she continued, "you go a bit too far. I feel like you want to be one of them," Roshan bluntly said what she surmised from Sadru's behavior.

Her ability to read Sadru's moods and passion often exposed his internal dialogue to her: she had read his desire of identification with the workers.

"Yes, I am one of them. I am a Marxist, we believe in declaring our solidarity with the workers of this world!" declared Sadru.

"Eh *Khuda*, what has got into your head now, *bhai?*" she said, shifting her head from left to right, "What is this all about? Is this whole nonsense anything to do with your weekend trips to the Hill for the last six months?" she inquired, condescendingly, as though she was the mother now.

"You know I am not stupid, Sadru. I know what is going on in the country. All this talk about African socialism we read in the papers. Africa for Africans! All these recent trips by the president to Russia, Cuba, and China, talk by the MPs about changes. All this noise about nationalizing banks, factories, and businesses," Roshan rattled on, surprising Sadru.

"Yes, there will changes, but don't worry, Roshan. It won't affect us," said Sadru, trying to diffuse the discomfort between them, but then decided to be direct.

Sadru took his eyes off the road, turned to Roshan, and assertively said, "I don't wish to discuss this. I can manage the workers fine. If there is a problem, you let me know. I will handle it, but my relationship with them will be what I please."

Neither Roshan nor Sadru wanted confrontation; each felt that it was best to let it ride. Both voiced what had to be said. In many ways an inexplicable symbiotic relationship had developed between the two: Roshan needed him as the man around the business to deal with the workers, to fill the void from Noordin's absence, a family person around whom she felt connected, secured; for Sadru she had been a nurturing sister, in absence of their parents. Even at his age, her only surviving family, she filled a void of insecurity.

So they drove in silence the rest of the way, passing mildewed, white buildings along the Nkrumah Road through the center of the city, past the Red Cross building across from the Hellenic Center towards their secured households of the Upanga Road.

After Sadru dropped Roshan and parked the car outside her house, he walked to his flat on Aly Khan Road. He took a shower, changed into a loud African *kitenge* shirt with a picture of the president in the front of the shirt with a small print at the bottom — *Uhuru na Umoja (Freedom and Unity)*. He left his flat and marched along Aly Khan Rd, past the grand mosque — where a stream of fashionably dressed Asians embarked from their flashy cars to attend the Friday evening prayers — towards the Palm Beach Hotel for a couple of drinks.

On his way past the imposing mosque, Sadru thought this would be his ideal grounds for recruitment of new converts to spread the wisdom and evangelize the Marxist ideology to the vulnerable, credulous and impressionable rebelling youngsters of his community.

Last Friday, after his two bottles of Tusker beer at the Palm Beach Hotel and after the mosque prayers were over, he stopped to eat freshly grilled *miskakis* sold by African vendors outside the mosque compound. This was where youngsters of both sexes from his community mingled, and others outside their community, boys interested in courting the fashion conscious girls of his lot, congregated and socialized.

Then he had met three youngsters — each in their 6th form at the parochial secondary school. In them he had sowed the bait and seeds of curiosity; now it was time to nurture it.

He had worked out how to woo them into his world. But first he had to impress them, win their confidence, and cultivate a sense of deference towards him. Sadru knew he could rely on his recollection skills of quoting passages of text, verbatim, from all the leftist literature he had voraciously consumed. His association with the local intelligentsia at Hill would furnish glamour and impress his newly found pupils and instill in them his stature and his know how.

He wasn't some Asian shopkeeper's ignorant son; he was worldly, knew important and erudite people at the Hill, had brushed shoulders with political dignitaries, and looked like none other than Dennis Brutus! He was an "intellectual", he believed.

Standing next to Joseph Kitamba — the portly African vendor selling *miskakis* — were Sadru's potential "recruits," dressed in their Friday suits, talking, sweating and eating spicy morsels of tender meat cooked over hot charcoal.

At the other end of the line of vendors selling eatable items was the Asian seller, Kabul, as he came to be known, of *miskakis*, who had deprived and wooed Joseph Kitamba's Asian clientele when Kabul set up shop. As most of Joseph's former clients preferred to give business to their own kind, a sort of bitter rivalry had ensued between Joseph and Kabul. A few words were exchanged, racists expletives hurled at each other and threats of spells of *uchavi* towards Kabul and his family were declared by Joseph.

But business went as usual, with market economics at their smallest scale, taking a natural course – or others would lament unfair and predatory business practices.

"Eh, Sadru, man, back for some *nyama* after a few pints," said Moez, the most vocal and flippant of the three youngsters he had met a week before.

Sadru shook hands with everybody, including Joseph, who put three skewers made from bicycle wheel spokes of *miskakis* onto the sizzling hot grill upon Sadru's request. Plumes of aromatic smoke sizzled into the air from the fatty juices dripping onto the hot charcoal as the flames engulfed the skewers. Joseph diligently attended to all the skewers, turning and shifting them from the center to the side as they became ready for consumption, brushing them with savory hot African chili sauce, whose effects can only be felt — and endured — the next morning in the toilet.

"Yes, man, beers and *nyama* go well," said Sadru, smiling.

"I like the shirt," complimented Firoz, who was quiet and observant. He was the smartest of all, the only child of a young professional couple. His mother is a nurse at the Aga Khan Hospital, and his father an accountant with Coopers and Lybrand. Both were educated in England, where they had met. They returned to Dar after their respective courses to "build the nation" — as Firoz's mother had told his new husband who wanted to remain in London.

"*Uhuru na Umoja*. That is what we need!" exclaimed Sadru, showing the clenched fist in the air, a universal sign of the workers' power struggle.

"How come you did not come inside the mosque today?" asked Moez.

"What was today?" inquired Sadru, affecting ignorance.

"Man, it was *Khushali*," said Salim who knew Sadru's sister. She lived two flats down the same row from Salim. Salim's father owned a chicken farm in Kinondoni and sold eggs to the local tenants. He also supplied poultry to the local Asian-owned supermarkets. Roshan had a weekly standing order of a tray of freshly picked and graded eggs. And when his father would bring his delivery van home on

Saturdays, Salim would deliver them to her house, just as he did for other tenants in the Upanga flats.

"Ah, I don't believe in all that nonsense," declared Sadru, dismissing its auspiciousness with a gesture of his hand.

Except for Firoz, Moez and Salim were a bit surprised at this answer, but did not display any visible signs of adversity. They were curious and drawn at his bold statements. They rarely heard or met people who challenged the pillars of their unshakeable faith.

"So what do you believe in?" probed Firoz.

"I simply don't believe in religion," replied Sadru.

"I am a Marxist. We Marxists are atheists. You see all those people over there?" said Sadru, pointing his finger towards the inner compound of the mosque where cars were lined up to carry back families home from their religious rituals, "They all are ignorant masses. Karl Marx said that religion is like an opiate for the masses. I would rather die than take the opium," added Sadru, raising a dripping skewer of *miskakis* to his mouth, drawing one morsel of delicious meat with his teeth and relishing its taste.

"I believe in questioning everything," declared Sadru with professorial confidence. He was now in command and ready to parrot his phrases.

"That is the essence of being a radical. You should never believe what someone tells you. What Marx said about the essence of a radical is their 'uncompromising critical evaluation of all that exists.'"

"So why should we believe you?" challenged Firoz.

"I like that, Firoz," replied Sadru, "You see: Firoz is *thinking*. He is evaluating all I said. And that is what Marx basically meant by 'critical evaluation of all that exists.'"

"This is d-e-e-p, man," giggled Moez, and added, "How many beers you had, eh?"

These effectual exchanges of Sadru impressed the youngsters, especially his ability to quote long passages of incomprehensible text from Karl Marx's *Communist Manifesto* — on aspects of religion, social evolution, on class, and the sanctity of work, where he brutally chastised his community as bourgeoisies and the ruling elite controlling most means of production.

Sadru continued parroting for the next hour. He captivated his credulous pupils who mostly listened, at times dazzled with his eloquence: everything Sadru had heard from his weekend seminars, all he had read about the leftist philosophers was being distilled and carefully and tactfully instilled into his young comrades.

Sadru developed a small following of young, impressionable followers, a band of disciples, the likes of Moez, Firoz, and Salim. They held him in regard; their awe for him matched and echoed Sadru's initial experience at those first weekly communist gatherings, in the company of intellectuals and luminaries at the Hill.

Just as then, he was a pupil — the tutorials of the Communist Party were meant for recruits like him — so now, they were for his young recruits. Never before had he experienced this surge of power and control and self-confidence; it fueled his missionary zeal as a purveyor of Marxist ideology.

For months, his recruitment continued every week on Friday evenings outside the compounds of the mosque, amidst capitalist activities of selling and buying. Soon, word reached the rank and file of the administrative echelons of the mosque — the local community council members — that Sadruddin Kassam, Roshan's younger brother, was a fledging member of the Communist party and was "corrupting" the young minds, urging them to question the fundamentals and teachings of their faith, challenging the apotheosis of the imam, encouraging them to rebel against their parents' business activities, and preaching the utopian virtues of socialism.

So a committee of council members was summoned to urge and request the imam to excommunicate Sadru. But the imam had other pressing matters to worry about; he urged the council members to settle and mediate the matter through other means.

Instead of excommunication, the council members approached Roshan Kassam, the widow of Noordin Kassam, who before his sudden death served as a *mukhi* for some of the *majlasis*. They revealed her brother's transgressions, admonishing her unequivocally, using the imam as their authority to carry its maximum impact. They cautioned her that any further inciting acts of communal disharmony among the young and vulnerable by Sadru would not be tolerated. And if the proselytizing of communist propaganda was not ceased immediately by Sadru Kassam, the ultimate and unfortunate retribution would be complete ostracism of the entire Kassam family, including her two children.

All through the admonition, Roshan patiently listened to the threat from the local council president, in the company of the local mosque *mukhi* in an adjacent room to the small mosque library. She held back swelling waves of anger from the embarrassment, all channeled to her nail-digging grip on the wooden arm rests of the upholstered chair. So intense was her clutch that by the time the ordeal was over, she had shreds of scaled wood stuck under her broken fingernails.

At home, in the privacy of her room, Roshan sobbed and thought of phoning her children in London but held back, realizing they were writing their final exams. It would be a distraction. She wanted to tell them that she had enough of Sadru and would desire for them to return and replace him. With their presence, they would let Sadru go as was agreed. Let him survive elsewhere with his Marxist ideals, his workers' mentality, without the wages and comforts she offered him.

The next day, being the last Friday of the month, meant truck loads of scrap metal delivery all day long. Sadru's revealing events and the meeting with the mosque council members had deprived her of her sleep. She was easily irritable, but maintained her calm when Sadru came to the flat for their joint ride.

On their way to work, they stopped at the bank to withdraw a large sum of money: 200,000 shillings. The week before, they were contacted by an Asian businessman in Morogoro who said he would be sending several truck loads of scrap metal. All that metal would require large amounts of cash. Roshan was restive that morning, carrying this large sum of money.

In the neighboring country of Kenya, particularly in the city of Nairobi, a spat of recent daylight muggings and gun robberies aimed at Asians had taken its toll of victims. Such events took a life of its own, exaggerated as it conveyed from one family to another, one community to another, each adding its own flavor of drama and horror. It was no surprise why Asians were the target: they had the money.

The bank opened at 8:00 AM. There was a crowd, mainly Asians, waiting outside. The familiar African woman bank teller smiled at Roshan and Sadru, and handed them their usual lump sum of money. Roshan took the lump and put them inside an oil-stained, decrepit brown paper bag. On top of the money, she placed her lunch of curry and rice in a plastic container and some yogurt and a bunch of bananas, concealing its contents.

"Sadru, you carry it," she handed him the bag, her hand slightly shaking.

Sadru obliged, and they both cautiously walked outside the bank into the bright morning light. It was mildly pleasant, but in a matter of hours when the sun ascends high above the sky at noon — and the humidity saturates the air, creating an invisible floating blanket of trapped heat over the city of Dar — its oppressive heat will torture its inhabitants.

Inside the car, Sadru placed the brown paper bag underneath Roshan's car seat. They drove past the shop-lined Samora Michel Avenue towards the road to the airport. She recalled the events of last night. She had decided not to confront Sadru but inform him, plead to him to stop the nonsense, to leave the youngsters alone.

"Sadru," she said softly, consciously avoiding any tone of confrontation, "the mosque *mukhi* and the council president talked to me yesterday."

"What about?"

"Well, *bhai*, they know about your activities," she said, using words carefully.

"Activities?"

"Yes, the youngsters you talk to every Friday after the prayers. They said that you are turning them into Marxists," she pretended to laugh.

"They warned me if that if you don't stop this, they will ostracize us all," said Roshan plainly. You know what that means for us," she added.

"I don't care," declared Sadru, without looking at her.

"Yes, you may not, but I live in this community, and so do your nephews," Roshan replied, still composed.

"What a bunch of cowards," Sadru mocked and continued, "Why can't they talk to me? Are they afraid they cannot handle me? So they choose the soft spot like you!"

"Sadru, I don't interfere in your life. This has to stop," she pleaded with him.

"Roshan, some of these youngsters are doing their Advanced levels. They are not children. They have minds of their own. They can think for themselves!" said Sadru.

Roshan tried to be reasonable, and told herself she must employ subliminal means to stop Sadru's self delusional "activities" outside the mosque on Fridays until her children returned in a month's time. After that, she would be in a stronger position to deliver Sadru an ultimatum. It would be best for the family, for everybody's interests, to let Sadru go.

"Sadru, stop this for me, for your nephews, for Mom and Dad," she pleaded, again.

"I am not going to, Roshan. I am who I am. If your council members think I am corrupting the hearts and minds of the young, what do you think they do at their night classes every day? It is not any different. It is all a matter of perspective," asserted Sadru.

Roshan turned the car into the dirt road heading towards the compound. The road was deserted, except for an occasional car leading to business compounds, and few Africans walking towards their destination further down the road.

She pulled the car at the closed gate. The morning *Askari* was nowhere to be seen. He normally sat inside the compound by the gate, and only opened the gate from the inside each morning for Roshan and Sadru, but today his chair was empty.

She honked once, then twice, but to no avail, then one more time, getting impatient.

"Where is the *askari?*" she asked, throwing her arms in the air, the car engine still running.

"Perhaps he is inside, or in the bathroom, or sick," replied Sadru.

Roshan replied, "If he was sick, the night *askari* would be here, at least. He is supposed to release him." She knew the protocol.

"Maybe he went to get something to eat," said Sadru, not looking at her.

"Well, we are not paying him to eat, while I am waiting in the car!" she said irritably, slamming the open palm of her hands on the steering wheel.

Just then a gray, beat-up jeep pulled up behind them, trapping them between the gate and the car. Two masked men, dressed in worn-out army fatigues, jumped from the jeep, one carrying a small pistol and the other an AK-47 semi-automatic gun. They each rushed to either side of the Peugeot 504, while the third — the driver — sat in the getaway jeep, gunning the engine, pinning the Peugeot against the gate.

The first gunman with an AK-47 put the gun to Roshan's head from the open driver's window and demanded, "Weh *muhindi!* Where is the money? Give us your money or I will kill you!"

Roshan and Sadru realized just too late what had just happened. Sadru turned white, cold sweat forming on his forehead. He seamed paralyzed while the second gunmen had his pistol pointed at him from the passenger side.

Roshan stayed calm and said, "Here take it," she handed the first gunmen her leather purse.

The second gunman hit Sadru with the back of the pistol butt, breaking the skin on his head. Blood streamed down the side of his face from his open wound.

"Tell your sister to hand over the brown paper bag or she will die!" the second gunman menacingly commanded.

Sadru pleaded to Roshan in their language. "Give it to them Roshan. They are serious. They will kill both of us."

In the distance, from the far left, a small pickup truck full of African workers in its open space in back approached from the other side of the dirt road towards them. Roshan spotted it from the corner of her eyes.

She reckoned that she could back up her car fiercely into the blocking jeep just as the truck is close to them, creating an accident, a scene that would catch the approaching car's attention. It was her plan to draw the pickup truck into the scene. That way, she hoped, the thugs would panic and flee.

"Give us the bag you *muhindi* whore!" demanded first gunman with the semi-automatic.

Tell your sister to hand over the brown paper bag. Those words repeated and echoed in Roshan's mind amidst the hold out. How did they know I was his sister? How did they know about the brown paper bag? All kinds of thoughts raced through Roshan's mind. She was convinced this was an inside job; someone from the compound knew this ritual, or someone from the bank, or God forbid, she thought, Sadru! She could not believe at the realization that it could be Sadru. Why would Sadru insist on giving them the money without any resistance?

The approaching pickup truck was within visible distance, Roshan noticed from the corner of her peripheral vision.

Now, Roshan, she told herself. Now or never, engage in reverse, floor the pedal, ram into the jeep and push it out of the way. In moments the approaching car would be in clear proximity of the crime scene. There would be chaos, the gunmen would panic and may flee. She was not going to give these thugs the money, she had resolved. And if any of it was Sadru's doing, she would deal with him.

She put the car in reverse, and floored the accelerator; the Peugeot 504 lurched backwards, ramming into the jeep, almost lifting itself off the road. The getaway jeep was too heavy; it hardly moved.

Just then a series of quick short successive shots rang out like small fire crackers one heard on days of Hindu Diwali festival every year in the city center, near the Odeon Cinema and around the Hindu residential areas.

The first gunman had open fired with his AK-47, blowing off the side and back of Roshan's head. A large portion of the back of her skull and spongy, reddish-white brain tissue landed on Sadru's lap, followed by her limp body with most of the rear and side of her head missing. Blood and brain tissue splattered across the black dash board and wide windshield.

Sadru gasped a couple of times in sheer terror, his mouth wide open, and then he screamed, but his cries of horror were snuffed when the second gunman shot him twice: once in the face and then in the neck. The first bullet shattered his jaw, the second penetrated his neck and severed his major artillery. Blood sprouted from his bullet wound like a small water hose. With every heave of the breath, life drained out of Sadru. He slumped forward, but his body was restrained from the seat belt.

Roshan's lifeless corpse lay on Sadru's lap; blood from his facial wounds trickled and dripped into Roshan's shattered skull, her dark hair matted in thick blood with bits of white brain tissue, her blank, lifeless eyes wide open, starring into nothingness.

The first gunman opened Roshan's door and reached under the seat for the brown paper bag. By then, the pickup truck, which was a few yards away, had reduced its speed. The Arab driver in the car realized what had just happened.

The first gunman open fired at the encroaching pickup truck's tires, bursting them. The workers in the back screamed as the truck came to a violent and awkward halt. They all cowered in the back, covering their ears and heads with their arms. The Arab driver ducked under the leg space of the passenger side, fearing for his life from what he just witnessed: cold-blooded murders.

Both gunmen got into their getaway car and sped away with the loot, leaving Sadru bleeding to death from his fatal wounds. By the time the ambulance and police arrived — summoned by the Arab driver of the shot-down pickup truck — Sadru had slipped into coma, from loss of blood, and was fighting for his life. The moment the ambulance arrived outside the hospital emergency ward, Sadru died. The *sirens* of the police and ambulance came to his rescue, but the *bullets* of the gunmen killed him.

Three days later, Roshan's two children arrived from London, for the second time in the year — this time to bury their mother. They were buried at their community graveyard.

At the Hill, Sadru's comrades had a small memorial session. One of his young recruits, Firoz, eulogized and read a poem from Dennis Brutus' collection: *Sirens and Bullets*.

Sadru's young army of Asian comrades was the next generation of true intellectuals, who embraced the ideals and visions of the country. And Sadru's spirit continued after his violent death.

A Household Divided

Part II

One Sunday morning in August of 1971, about six months before Sadru Kassam, a self-proclaimed Marxist and his enterprising, wily sister were brutally murdered in an armed robbery outside their scrap metal business in Magomeni, Sadru and I rode the local bus to his weekly Communist Party gathering at the Hill. It was my first attendance with him; many eventually followed.

On that particular day — the bus was sparsely occupied with disengaged and rueful African passengers, perhaps returning home from their nightly jobs — Sadru turned to me, his wistful eyes and his drawn face showing concern and somberly said, "Not everyone sees the country with the same eyes."

It took me few minutes to absorb what he meant. I thought, perhaps, he was referring to African passengers on the bus — what and how their perception of the country was different from ours.

"But that is inescapable. We all are different, come from different backgrounds, have different aspirations."

"Right," Sadru elaborated, "That is the whole premise of *Mwalimu's Arusha Declaration:* to bring commonality and equality among all races, to mitigate the class and tribal barriers, to provide, if you will, a common set of eyes, a vision, to everyone so they all see the country with the same eyes."

"'A common set of eyes...' I never thought of it that way."

He smiled, pleased with himself for his insight, summarizing the universal human tenets of the declaration into its simplistic and poetic metaphor for his pupil. Sadru had taken me under his wing, more so than other youngsters my age, who were drawn to him for his unprecedented provocative and rebellious stances against the community affairs and his left-wing politics. But when time came for taking action, like attending the weekend seminars or distributing literature, they deserted him, fearing their parents' retribution.

On that day, at the gathering, I had met a black Jamaican academic, Clive Robertson, from the University of West Indies. Sadru had introduced me to him, shortly before his talk on the political effects of the political message in Reggae music in the trench towns of Jamaica.

"Clive, meet my protégé," said Sadru, proudly presenting me to Clive.

"Oh, you must be Firoz," said Clive, extending his hand, and added, "Sadru has talked about you. I am glad you can join us."

Clive was an elegant and handsome man — tall and slim and smooth-skinned. He wore a loosely-fitted *kitenge* shirt, contouring his athletic body. He was well spoken with a tinge of typical West Indian lilt, and his clarity of thought and persuasive oratory skills had impressed me.

A few days before Sadru's memorial at the Hill, organized by his comrades, Clive Robertson phoned me at home, and asked me to speak at Sadru's eulogy. I recall Clive saying,

"Sadru was very fond of you. It would be an honor if you could speak a few words at the memorial."

And so I did. I read from a collection of poems by Dennis Brutus — *Sirens and Bullets* — at the memorial services for Sadru Kassam who looked like Dennis Brutus and had altered the course of my life – and in more ways than one, divided our household.

My household was uncommon within the Asian immigrant community. Both my parents were university educated in England. They were professionally successful in their careers and had elected to have a small family, even though, historically, almost all Asian families in East Africa had at least three or four children.

But my parents' individual vocations were their priority. My father worked as a certified accountant for a British firm Coopers & Lybrand in Dar. He was well-placed in the company and he received comfortable compensation. His clientele comprised of prominent Asian, African, and European businessmen.

Contrastingly, my mother worked in the health services sector. She was the head registered nurse at the Aga Khan Hospital, and taught at the Muhimbili Nursing School. She also headed the government's efforts to establish rural health and nutritional programs for women in various remote villages in the interior.

Her job was trying, for she traveled, often for days on end, to some very remote areas in the interior. Her commitment to her profession and advancement of women, of all races, was contagious and admirable.

Being their only child, Mom and Dad focused to nourish the best in me — and undoubtedly, they did.

They had great hopes and dreams for me, especially my father. He had wished for me — like himself — to study abroad, in England, after my secondary education; he had aspirations for me to establish myself, professionally, in England, to where his family had emigrated. Through his professional connections with his employer in Dar, he had made the required financial arrangements for my university education.

I had finished my 6th form, and upon my father's insistence, sat for the Cambridge exams in Nairobi. For my A-levels, I read economics, mathematics, philosophy, and history, and had received distinctions, both in the locally administered government exams as well as in exams administered by the Cambridge University in England.

Not surprisingly, my father implored — and I acquiesced — to apply to various universities in England. I got accepted at Imperial College of London and Oxford, Trinity College. When he received my acceptance letter, he had rushed home early from work and appeared in my room.

"Firoz," he excitedly said, as he entered my room, "you are going to Oxford!" brandishing a white envelope hurriedly ripped at the perforations.

"I am so proud you, son!" he added, wearing a proud smile, blushing, as if my acceptance fulfilled what he had dreamed of, but could not achieve. Parents always see their children as an extension of their egos.

"Mom will be home soon from work. We shall celebrate, go out for dinner, have some champagne," he said effusively.

That evening after my mother returned from work, we went to Oyster Bay Hotel for dinner. My father had intimated to me that he wanted to keep it a secret from mom until during dinner, so I did not mention anything to her when she arrived later than her normal time.

When we arrived for dinner at the Oyster Bay Hotel, the gracious African waiter seated us at a corner table upstairs in the open terrace, with a magnificent view of the coconut tree-lined white sandy beaches of the bay — luminescent under the full African moon — as the waves disbursed their phosphorous foam along the shoreline. In the background, out at sea, a dozen flickering flames of the lantern from the fisherman's *dhows* proclaimed their presence in the vastness of the shimmering Indian Ocean. And in the far distance, we could see the glimmering lights that outlined the anchored steamers awaiting their call to berth at the harbor.

We each ordered peppered steak, our favorite entrée, and a bottle of champagne.

"Well, what is this all about?" asked Mom, looking first at Dad, and then at me.

"This is a defining moment for our son. All those years of hard work and toil, our laser focus on education and lofty academic achievements have come to fruition for Firoz: he got admitted to Oxford. I want to express my unbounded gratitude to your mom for her unwavering encouragement all these years," Dad pronounced proudly.

Dad had a way with words; like an actor with timely elocution and diction, he could emolliate his audience, could evoke the desired emotions in them. He was a natural orator — a charmer. Why he ended up as an accountant belies his natural abilities as a plausible diplomat. Along with his good looks — he was tall and slender, with a full head of graying hair, giving him a distinguished look — and his comfort with rhetoric, he would have made a good spokesperson.

"I want to propose a toast to you, Firoz. Tonight, your mom and I feel ascended to the lofty heights of parental bliss. Cheers!" said Dad, lifting his glass with bubbling champagne.

"How wonderful, Firoz," my mom retorted and raised her glass to her lips. Her face spoke of motherly pride.

"So let's return back to reality from our lofty parental heights," Mom chuckled, looking at me directly, and said: "Well, how do you feel about it?"

Being a weekday, the terrace was sparsely crowded, unlike on the weekends, where one must reserve a table in advance. A few Europeans — mostly English speaking — occupied a couple of tables along the terrace facing the ocean; an Asian couple, seated in the middle of the terrace with clear view of our table, constantly stared in our direction. Next to them was a large table with boisterous young couples of mixed races, perhaps celebrating somebody's birthday. A few smartly-dressed Africans sat at the bar nursing their beers.

I mustered up the courage to shatter — if not my mom's, but definitely, my father's hopes and wishes for me.

"I got accepted at the Hill to study law, and I am seriously considering it. It is where I want to be for the next four years."

Dad looked at me incredulously, as if I had uttered blasphemy.

"Why would you want to go to the Hill, when one of the best universities in the world accepted you?" inquired Dad with a tone of utter astonishment, if not a condescending disgust.

"Because I have met friends at the Hill, because I want to be close to home."

"You know you have family in England. All my brothers live there. You have cousins your age, too. It is not as if you going to an alien land. During summer holidays, you can always come back to Dar.

"As for friends at the Hill, if you are referring to that leftist quack Sadru Kassam and his posse you befriended, they are nothing but a bunch of left wing loonies and hacks, full of empty Communist jargon. I have seen their lot during my university days in London," said Dad with derision, and then added, "They are completely useless. All of them, living off the dole or dependent on their family inheritance for financial support, while purporting grandiose and utopian ideals of communism. I say hypocrisy at its worst.

"This is an once-in-a-lifetime opportunity to be a part of the larger world, at the *center* of an important world, to be part of the tradition of leaders from the developing nations, former colonies, who went to this institution, achievers who have made their mark in this world. And you want to throw away this chance to attend some mediocre African university in the bush because you have befriended some leftist friends here?" said Dad, clearly irritated and contemptuous.

Mom reached over with her hand and placed it on Dad's, and gently squeezed and tapped it, suggesting to Dad to calm down. She turned to me and said: "Look, Firoz, you have some thinking to do. It is not as if you have to decide tonight. Sleep over it for the next few days or a week. You must explore all your options. In the end, it will be your decision, and you will have to live with it."

That evening she looked a lot younger than her age, clad in a knee-length, tightly-fitted red dress on her full, shapely body. A black shawl concealed her exposed shoulders. Her shoulder-length black hair was drawn back into a tight bun, revealing her shapely and delicate face, where lines of endurance were masked behind the makeup. She looked classically sensual.

From his trips to London, Dad always returned with the latest dresses, shoes, and purses, and whenever they went out to one of Dad's cocktail parties, they both dressed fashionably. I sensed it was more my Dad's desire than hers; for work and elsewhere without Dad, she dressed casually.

After Dad's acerbic sermon, I felt small. I wanted to go and hide in the bathroom, or under the table. Dad was explosive, visibly upset. His face wore the mask of disappointment and betrayal. Underneath was the same sentiment I had sensed when I elected to attend Sadru Kassam's memorial at the Hill instead of accompanying him on a fishing trip organized by his colleagues from the firm. Then, he had remained calm, but not tonight.

The rest of the meal, we ate in silence, with only the clatter of silverware and hearty laughter from the Africans at the bar punctuating our uncomfortable silence. My mother made attempts at small talk about her medical excursions of the day and her meetings with the health ministry officials and her plans about traveling to the interior for setting up rural clinics. She appeared very excited about this undertaking. It gave her immense confidence and sense of pride and achievement; it validated her beliefs.

Dad was initially reluctant about her spearheading this government effort of rural health clinic development. He seemed uncomfortable with Mom disappearing in the "bush" — as he referred to it — for days, sometimes weeks, with some African health officials, but Mom was fiercely independent and asserted her ways, and Dad acquiesced. Her frequent absence gave Dad freedom and time to enjoy his excursions: golf with partners and clients at the Gymkhana, weekend fishing trips to the islands, cocktail parties, and business trips abroad. It was mutually beneficial, and suited their independent temperaments.

Now and then, the cool breeze from the Oyster Bay would surge, filling the air above the terrace with salty scent.

After the meal, we drove home in silence. During the night, I could hear muffled voices from their bedroom. I could not make out the words, but obviously they were discussing – or arguing about — my fate. Innate human curiosity prevailed and I stealthy walked across the unlit hallway and placed my ear against the closed bedroom door.

"This would not have happened if we had remained in London after our courses. We could have raised him there. But you had to come back here because of your misguided and misplaced sympathies and loyalties. Some silly, idealistic notion of building a nation," said Dad.

"Stop patronizing me," Mom yelled, "I don't have misplaced sympathies for Africans!" retorted Mom, "I returned because I felt I belong here and that I could do something useful in my country. And damn well, I am heading projects that are fruitful for which I am proud. And the people I work with applaud that. Must you make everything political?" implored Mom.

"'My country!'" mocked Dad. "This is not our country. You really believe deep in your heart that these *karias* give a shit about us *muhindis?* If you do, then your lot is self-delusional. History will obliterate and ignore our contributions. Asians will not be attributed for what we did here," said Dad.

"In a way, it negates all our contributions, doesn't it, if you just leave, walk away silently instead of staying and asserting, doesn't it? Look, Nazir, I am not in a mood to engage in a political discussion with you. It is our son we are talking about. If Firoz wishes to remain here and study here, then it is his decision. Why must you chart his life? Why must he live your aspirations, your unfulfilled dreams? You hardly gave the poor boy a chance to explain tonight why he wanted to study here. Instead, you just chastised him," she added.

"His decision to attend the Hill is irrational. It is affected by factors he barely comprehends. The lofty, utopian ideals of Marxist ideology are profoundly and humanly desirable. But that is theoretical: the economic *realities* of this country dictate alternate forms of economic growth. He is brainwashed by those communist friends of Sadru. His education here is going to be worthless, full of grandiose, leftist, empty slogans. You cannot deny the weight of educational credentials from Oxford," declared Dad.

"It is a matter of perspective. Are you suggesting that nurses I teach and train here are less qualified, less intelligent, less competent than nurses who graduate from abroad?" asked Mom. "I am going downstairs to do some work."

I heard muffled footsteps from inside approaching the closed bedroom door.

I dashed back to my room in frenzy, jumped in the bed, and slid under the covers, pretending to be fast asleep.

Within seconds, I heard Mom enter my room to check. I wondered if she detected that I was outside listening; or whether she just came to see if I was awake for a chat. I reckoned she felt I was annoyed from the dinner confrontations, and perhaps I wanted to chat, without Dad being present. But I pretended I was fast asleep.

Normally, I am awake late into the night, reading, acquiring knowledge about the larger world, a distant world, only vivid in words.

The events of the last few hours kept me awake. I was upset, but failed to comprehend what caused me grief. Was it guilt from betrayal? Was I the cause of parental disharmony? Would my household be devoid of conflicts had I not met Sadru Kassam, and not let him recruit me into his circle of friends?

No answers came to me.

I admired my Mom immensely; her self-assuredness and boldness, her core human values, her commitment to her vocation, and her communal health and educational projects for the betterment of the populace-at-large were peerless then. She was purely motivated by her belief and passion in empowering the less fortunate women of all races.

Never before had I witnessed my parents so polarized and embroiled in their political sentiments; it was as if all these years, they led and played duplicitous roles: a public life of filial nurturing and familial harmony; and a private life of visceral conflict that manifested itself only behind closed doors, shielded from their beloved ones.

That night, I became resolute about my decision to attend the Hill. The following morning, after a restless night, when I came downstairs, I declared — at the breakfast table where my mom and dad sat — my intentions to remain in Dar and go to the Hill, and nothing was going to alter my decision.

Dad said with tone of utter dejection, "You disappoint me, son. An opportunity of a lifetime, being cast away merely because of your imbecile ideology is laughable. You shall regret it one day, but I won't be around then."

And he left for work, wearing that familiar mask of dejection on his face, which appeared each time in my presence.

All this happened more than a year ago. Since then, I have been estranged from my father; whenever I went home, upon Mom's insistence, I planned my visits when he was away, out of town, or on a weekend fishing trip. On term breaks, I remained at the Hill.

Mom made efforts to visit me at the Hill during my first year. Sometimes, she would drive alone, at other times, she would be accompanied by her African colleagues from the health ministry. Occasionally during her visits, we went to the African local joint, Karibu Café, a club down the main road at the edge of campus for lunch or dinner.

On a weekend night — Saturdays — students and faculty patronized the joint; its circular glazed dance floor under the open sky provided ample space for dancing, and the dimly-lit African thatched hut-like enclosures with tables around the floor's periphery provided secrecy and anonymity for courting. The hypnotic African musical beats played till early morning hours; its tunes often echoed in the hallways of the nearby residence halls closer to the main road. Sweaty bodies, joined and embraced at the hips, gyrated sensually to the rhythmic beats all night.

∭

Two years went by. The mood in the country had altered. It was a trying times for Asians in the country — especially after the forced expulsions in nearby Uganda by the raving madman, General Idi Amin. The madman's actions — though condemned harshly by our *Mwalimu* as "crimes against humanity" — silently validated the indigenous African's resentments towards us here and in other neighboring countries.

With massive nationalization of many Asian retail enterprises and properties, it was evident that the psychological impact of it all had triggered fight-or-flight in many of us; it set in motion the wheels of the Asian exodus. Instantly, families began sending their elder sons abroad out of fears of a similar fate of our brethren in Uganda; applications for emigration flooded British, Canadian, Australian, and American consulates.

Undeniably for the Asian community, it was a tumultuous period of utter disharmony and insecurity: families disbursed, households divided, childhood friends lost, means of livelihood deprived, and a way of life erased.

At the time, I was at the end of my third year at the Hill, reading law. I was also a contributing writer and editor for the student law review. It was founded by an Asian professor of law, a renowned academic, an unwavering Marxist at heart, and an ardent and relentless supporter and preacher of Mwalimu's policies. I had met him during various Sunday meetings in the company of Sadru Kassam. He was unassailable; later I became his protégé and his mouthpiece.

Those of us (a small minority) who supported *Mwalimu's* polices were castigated as traitors within the community, notably our Asian finance minister who was *Mwalimu's* right-hand man, and spearheaded his economic agenda.

Over time, I had developed my circle of friends at the Hill and had cultivated my political and national identity. It set me apart from those at the Upanga flats where we lived. Some had left the country or hurriedly sent off to construct a paved path in the new land, much like their forefathers, who had come here from India. I often wondered what would be their fate in their newly-adopted land. Would they transport and take their Africa with them — just like how their forefathers brought their India to Africa – and remain staid?

One Sunday morning, the floor phone of the residence hall rang persistently. No one was answering, not even the residence hall student manager. I managed out of bed, hung over from the previous night, only to discover that I had a young African woman in my bed, fully clothed, sleeping next to me. I was the assistant resident hall manager, and one of the perks for all services and duties — including answering all phones when present on the floor — was that we were furnished with a single unit room on the top floor. They were tiny but adequate: a small study table, a miniature bunk bed, and a tiny closet.

There was a phone outside each manager's door unit for quick access; altogether, they were three phones on each floor — one at each end of the hallway, and one in the center.

Clearly, the ringing one was outside my unit. I went outside and answered the phone.

"Hello, this is Firoz, the assistant residence manager."

"Firoz, it is me. Did I wake you up?" asked Mom.

"Sort of."

"Can you come home today?" asked Mom.

"No, I cannot. Why? Is something wrong?"

My head hurt and felt heavy with each word I spoke. I felt nauseated standing — my tongue dry from dehydration, my hand sweaty, and my knees, weak and wobbly.

"I wanted to talk with you. It is about Dad and me," she said reluctantly.

The lingering heat in the hallway and the urine stench from the open bathroom made me sick. My empty stomach retched, and I fell to my knees, clinging to the phone attached to the silver cord with my clammy hands. I started to retch, the heaving movements of my stomach jettisoning whatever was left from the previous night of excessive imbibing.

"Firoz, Firoz, Firoz," echoed the earpiece.

I retched again and again like a sick dog, making gut-wrenching noises.

"Firoz, are you throwing up? Put someone on the phone, I will tell them what to do," Mom demanded, the nurse in her taking control of the situation.

"Yes…Yes…I am sick," I managed to speak up.

Right then, my bedroom companion appeared through the doorway.

"Weh, are you okay? Should I call for help?" she asked.

I extended the phone to her, feeling weak and limp as cold sweat appeared on my forehead, and blankness engulfed me. I heard faint noises of my companion saying yes to instructions over the phone.

A moment later, I felt a couple of strong hands around my arm pits carrying me off to the shower halls and keeping me propped up against the white tiled walls. The cold water from the shower drenched my dry body. The water rivulets from my forehead ran over my dry lips and I sucked them. My parched tongue hurt but it slowly quenched my thirst.

I barely recognized the two African male students from the floor who held me in the shower and later led me back to my unit.

The young African woman's lucid voice said, "Your mother said to drink lots of water, but don't go to sleep — just recline on your bed, and take small sips of water, not gulps. She asked me to stay here and not leave you unattended until she arrives."

The young African woman spoke to me in English and Kiswahili.

With each sip of water, I began to get my bearings, but my head felt bloated, like an oversized football, and each movement, each effort to converse, induced waves of throbbing pain.

"*Weh Muhindi! Una kunywa pombe kama mtembo. Uta kufa weh!*" she joked and giggled. (*You Asian! You are drinking booze like an elephant. You will die!*")

"I am Christina Mlingwa. I am studying education, my second year. Do you remember me from last night? We drank together at the Karibu Café," she inquired.

I gingerly shook my head suggesting no, and took a few more sips of water from the glass Christina kept on filling from the water fountain outside. I belabored our conversation with pain.

"What did I drink?" I managed.

"Konyagi and Tusker beer. You had a bottle and dozen beers."

"You didn't drink?"

"Not like you!" she giggled.

She was slender and athletic, perhaps my age, maybe younger, with smooth skin and an oval face with full lips. Her short, African curly hair was neatly braided into long strands across the top of her head to the back of her slender neck, where each strand tapered and rolled into tiny circular tufts of loose hair. She wore large, silver looped earrings that framed her face; she looked very fashionable in slacks and a short white blouse, and heeled shoes — probably her clubbing attire.

"How did we get here last night from the club? I do not remember anything."

"Of course you would not. We walked from the club with my girlfriends. We all helped you up. You were very affectionate at the club and then later, you became very sad. You sobbed for a bit. You were mumbling something about your father then were saying something in your language. When we laid you in bed, you held my hand, and pleaded not to leave you alone, so I stayed the night. Nothing happened. I am not the kind," she assured me.

I took more sips of water. Everything she described was blanked out from memory.

"Thank you, Christina."

Christina gave me a beaming smile and said, "I will leave as soon as your mother arrives. Your mother seemed very concerned. She must be a doctor or nurse, giving me exact instructions of what to do. She asked me to take your pulse and call the infirmary but I could not get hold of anyone there, so she suggested I knock on a couple of doors in the hallway and get some help to get you in the shower. She knew you had been drinking."

"Yes, she is the head of nursing at the Aga Khan Hospital and teaches at the Muhimbili Hospital Nursing School," I said with my eyes closed, keeping my head still, avoiding waves of the throbbing pain from head movements.

"Look, I don't want you to get into trouble. I won't mention anything about me spending the night here. I will just say I was visiting my boyfriend and saw you in the hall, sick," she said.

It was obvious why the precaution, the fabrication, the unspoken concern. She cast me into the basket of all other Asians, judged me with tinted lenses of race and prejudice, yet her concern was genuine.

I assured her not to worry about staying until my mother arrived.

"My mother is not any different from yours. She would want to express her gratitude to you for helping me. It is human, not racial," I said.

She took it in, smiled, and extended her hand towards me, fingers open, facing downwards, a gesture of trust. I gently reached and squeezed her extended fingers, and mumbled under my breath: *Asante sana*.

From the open door, I heard my mom's familiar voice, talking in Kiswahili to someone. The voices grew louder by seconds, and moments later, she appeared in the doorway in her Indian shirt over a faded, loosely-fitted designer jeans, and slippers, carrying her medical bag in one hand.

"Hello, Firoz. How do you feel?" she asked as she did with each patient during her rounds at the hospital.

She reached for my forehead, and then engaged in her professional routine of taking my vital signs with the tools of the medical trade.

"Well, you seem okay, but you are extremely dehydrated, as I suspected. You have to exercise caution. People have been known to die from alcohol poising and abuse in rural and urban areas. I can tell from your breath and your state that you over-indulged, Firoz," she said sternly, like a concerned mother, and smiled at Christina, who was leaning against the closet, smiling — and enjoying Mom's dealings with her patient.

Christina had a fixed smile on her face, the spectator's smirk one wears when their companion is being reprimanded by an authoritarian figure, like a teacher in high school. I wondered if she was enjoying the moment, if she found the whole affair comical. I became a bit self-conscious of my mom.

Mother reached inside the medical bag and handed out two white tablets to me and said, "These will relieve the headache."

"Remember, you suffer from chronic asthma. Such drinking binges can trigger a massive attack. Not very wise, dear," she said with her maternal tone.

"Ah mama eh…watato siku hizi," (*Oh, my mother, children these days!*) She managed a light-hearted laugh, closed the medical bag, and turned towards Christina.

"You must be Christina. I am very grateful to you." She reached out and grabbed both her hands, and thanked her profusely.

Then, she looked around the room and declared, "You need some fresh air in the room," and reached up and pushed out the jammed windows open, which normally remained closed and secured on top floors because of personal hazards, but mainly because insects and mosquitoes would fill up the room at night, drawn by illuminated rooms.

A waft of breeze gushed in. On a clear day from this top floor of the residence hall, you could see in the distance the vast Indian Ocean as it stretched to the horizon.

Mom asked Christina where her family was from and what she was studying. She mitigated Christina's initial anxiety and relaxed her, just as she would a young patient before pricking her with the deadly-looking syringe, with perfunctory motherly queries about her experience at the Hill and her being away from family.

Christina revealed she was from the Tanga region and her father was a civil servant with government sisal farms recently nationalized.

Meanwhile, I felt a lot better with the fresh breeze gushing through the open windows and restored lost bodily fluids.

Christina said she had to return to her dormitory for studies. Mother stood up and thanked her again, extending her arm, which Christina gently held it. While shaking it, she bent her right knee, slightly lowering her body, and nodded her head, like many youngsters would do in some African villages in respect for parents and elders. Mother reciprocated — she knew the ritual from her time in the interior — and tapped her head gently.

Mother said to Christina, "I hope we meet again in better circumstances."

Christina gave me her charming smile, exposing her flashing white teeth, and said, "*Kwaheri*. See you at the mess hall." And with that, she disappeared through the open door.

She left the room but her infectious smiling face, her fragrance, lingered in the room, even though I did not recall any moments of courtship, if there was any, from the previous night. She had branded her fleeting image inside me.

"Very sweet and respectful girl!" exclaimed Mom, her eyes showing genuine appreciation.

"Your girlfriend?" she joked

I was not going to elaborate on any details of what Christina had told me but I mentioned that I was at the Karibu Café with some friends from my class and she was there with hers. Somehow, we all ended up at the same table and I drank a bit too much. She and her friends brought me back to the dormitory, and she came back this morning to check on me. Her friends had said I was too drunk.

Mother gave me the worried look, which was justifiable, given my frail health and chronic asthma since childhood — for which I was reprieved, on strict medical terms, from the mandatory National Service. Because of my frail health, I was never proficient — or even played — any enduring sports. What I lacked in sports, I made up in academia.

"Well, that was very considerate of her. Maybe she likes you," Mom said, laughing, and then added, "Ironically, that is how I first met your father, at a university night club, years ago, in London when we friends all went out at night. I literally met him in his drunken stupor. Life has its curious serendipitous moments and encounters."

Then she went silent, melancholic, and looked out the window, and moments later, she turned, her eyes rueful and said, "There is something I have to tell you, Firoz, but not here. Let's go someplace. Let's go to Bahari Beach. You need something to eat as well," she insisted.

Food was the last thing on my mind. After all the retching earlier, my guts hurt and cramped.

"Come on, come on. Let's go. Fresh sea breeze and some tomato juice will do you wonders," she insisted, lifting the bed sheets, suggesting she wanted to leave immediately, perhaps the miniature enclosure suffocated her and she wished to be out in the open air.

We drove north in silence for less than ten kilometers, past the military barracks, on the main road to the Bahari Beach, a secluded resort beach area dotted with miniature African thatch huts with reclining chairs, dispersed along the coconut-tree-lined white sandy beaches.

The main resort building — a gigantic open thatched hut supported by large steel beams — was buzzing with activity around the dining and drinking area; African waiters — dressed in starched white pressed uniforms and white chef hats were crisscrossing each other with plates balanced on each hand — served their seated patrons. Most patrons were mainly Africans and Europeans, and a conspicuous group of Asians, scattered around the patio tables, with their families. As usual, the grannies wearing saris minded the kids; the males drank boisterously, while women sat quietly, with blank expressions, nursing their soft drinks.

Mom asked me to look for a hut on the beach while she went and ordered some soup and soft drinks for us. I found an isolated hut at the far end of the enclosed and marked beach area; its nearby huts were occupied. I placed a small *kikapu* that Mom had packed with towels and sundry of toiletries on the table attached to the hut, and flopped on the reclining chair.

By this afternoon hour, the white beach sand was bristling hot, and reflected the dazzling light from the November African sun; without sandals, walking a short distance, the sand could burn the inside of your soles.

A short distance away, mirages — of huts with people inside them and couples walking on the beach, swimming and frolicking in the water — shimmered. The gentle, intermittent breeze from the Indian Ocean subdued the oppressive humidity of the damp heat.

In the background, soft African beats flowed from the speakers, suspended from steel beams supporting the roof structure of the hut facing the beach. The incessant sounds of crashing waves, mixed with gentle salty ocean breeze, induced lethargy and hypnosis, so uniquely characteristic of many Dar Sunday afternoons during the hot season.

Shortly, mother appeared with a tray of drinks: a large tomato juice, water and ice, and egg sandwiches.

"I have ordered some chicken soup. They are a bit busy so it may be a while, but meanwhile, the juice will help you. How is your head?" she asked.

"A lot better. No medicine can match this," I said, gesturing with my arms towards the natural beauty surrounding us.

"Yes, we are blessed with this natural beauty. Many take it for granted until it is lost or changed," she said ruefully.

Something had been bothering Mom all morning; I sensed it when she spoke with me on the phone, when she was in my room, and when we drove in silence to the beach.

As if she was waiting for an opportune moment, a sedate place, to liberate herself from the weight of it all, she started talking in tender voice and measured sentences.

"Firoz, I am leaving your dad," she declared. "I have asked your dad for a divorce." She stared out into the distance at the ocean, her face withdrawn, solemn.

Such a declaration was unheard of within the community: a wife walking out of marriage, leaving her husband. But my family was not the usual lot. She did what pleased her; nothing was going to get in her way: husband, family, religion, community, or politics.

"Why, after all these years?" I asked.

"Over the years, we have grown apart, increasingly polarized on everything. With you not at home, we fight every moment together, so we avoid each other whenever possible, each of us works long hours. He takes frequent trips away, to Nairobi and London. I stay longer on trips to the interior on behalf of the ministry. We simply don't talk any longer. It is like we are living separate lives," she said, turning towards me from her reclining wooden beach chair.

"Even after all these years, he still blames me for bringing him back here. He maintains that we would have had a better life in England, that we would have not been subjected to all this pain of uncertainty. But I think he is wrong. England has its share of problems for people like us. At a deeper level, changes around here have affected him. He lost his investments in property with the Methas and Tejanis, his clients from the firm, in their joint beach hotel property up the coast when the government nationalized it.

"Many of his close clients, Asian businessmen and industrialists, lost their wealth saved over generations. His firm is closing shop. They offered him a transfer to Nairobi, but he asked for London. He has 'given up on Africa,' as he put it. What family he has, he claims, is slipping away from him. There is nothing left for him here any longer."

"By family, you mean us?" I asked

"Yes…yes," she said, nodding towards me.

"Where is Dad, now?"

"After I told him I wanted to divorce him, he was shaken, a bit broken. He hasn't turned up at home in the last week. Sooner or later, he will turn up. He will have to get his stuff. I am keeping the house," Mom asserted.

Signs of dusk appeared around the horizon where the Indian Ocean extended and dropped off into an abyss.

Mom talked for the rest of the time. She said, with a mournful but assured voice, that I had the right to know what had been going on behind the façade of household bliss. Only I kept them bound together, and when I shattered Dad's hopes and wishes — which is how Dad referred to my decision to attend the Hill instead of going to England — she told me, it was apparent he felt betrayed by us.

Over time, their squabbles and arguments became political; self-recriminations between them damaging and hurtful: he became obsessively critical about everything in the papers – social reforms and economic polices of the country, her rural health clinic projects with the ministry, the liberation movements in the south. It was, she said, unlike him, uncharacteristic of the Nazir she married and bore a child with; bitterness had engulfed and tarnished his intellect and vision — and everything from that stained glass of his eyes appeared flawed and worthless and substandard.

"Well, there you have it all," she said, with a sigh of relief, "I feel that you act much older than your age and would comprehend the complexities and the frailties of human nature. No matter what happens with Dad, or with us here, I will always be here for you, and together, we will stick it out," she said with the assuring voice of a head nurse, like she did with her patients, giving them hope of recovery, reigniting the extinguished sparkle in their wistful eyes.

Since that night of confrontation behind my parents' closed doors after the dinner at the Oyster Bay Hotel almost three years ago, I had realized the true nature of my parents' hidden relationship: ridden with conflicts and contradictions; uncompromising and differing ideals and goals. And the inevitability of it all, its resolution, declared by Mom today, was not surprising. As much as the mood of the political events around the country, I, too, was a contributing factor to the growing fractures of our beloved household which was now divided.

Mom suggested we leave soon, as she had to prepare to receive some donors from overseas and plan a trip to Subwanga, where she traveled frequently on behalf of the ministry of health, which was setting up a local health clinic funded by the World Health Organization.

Two weeks later, Mom left for the interior. She said she would be gone for couple of weeks. Dad had tried to ring me a couple of times, as I found out later, to bid farewell, but could never get hold of me. He had never visited me at the Hill — not even to drop me off the first day of student orientation.

He was leaving for London, a place where he felt, in his words, "larger and vital events about the world transpired," with no intention of returning back to the "bush" — ever. Part of me died inside, the part that was made of him, leaving a void, yearning to be filled.

For the rest of the week, I searched the cafeteria (our mess halls at the Hill), for signs of Christina, hoping to find solace within her, yearning for her to fill the void, longing for that flashing, beaming and welcoming smile, that hand gesture of acceptance as who I was.

Oyster Bay

Part I

"Oh, Jamil! Eh, Jamil!" she shouted from the kitchen, her domain of authority, as if summoning our servant, Moosa Ali, to interrogate him if he had finished the list of household chores assigned to him every morning.

From the kitchen doorway at the end of the white wall, the accustomed dense aroma of fried onions and Indian-curry spices wafted and stuffed the dining room.

"What, Ma?"

Her large and tall body, in a faded, ankle-length *kitenge* dress, appeared in the kitchen doorway. She stood there, arms by her side, smiling. Her full head of gray-streaked black hair was combed back and tied into a small bun, which accentuated her round, soft face and the shadows under her almond-shaped Indian eyes.

"Ah, you're here. I thought you were upstairs, resting," Mother said, still under the doorway.

"No, can't sleep, Ma. It's too hot today."

I returned to my newspaper and turned to the front section to read the much-talked-about upcoming event: the political summit among the front-line states to embolden the armed struggle against the racist regimes in southern African countries fighting liberation wars.

All the southern African exiled political celebrities — high ranking members of the liberation movements — were to attend this summit in Dar, to express their camaraderie, and renew their unrelenting commitment to their struggle. Security, the paper explained, was going to be heightened: armed guards at the airport, on the nearby streets of the summit hall, and on the rooftops of the annexed buildings. Already in town, on Samora Michel Avenue at night, armed guards with bomb-sniffing dogs were posted at offices of these liberation outfits.

Lately, our papers increasingly ran bolstering stories of damage inflicted by the guerillas on the white dominated regimes to countries south of the border. Our country housed the guerilla camps, which provided both logistical support and the air waves to voice the freedom struggle for our brethren in the south. In the evening on the radio, one heard moving freedom songs, cries for justice, and incendiary oratory from Karim Shivji of the liberation movement.

"Haa, did you ask Moosa to iron your clothes. Your suit?" she asked.

"Suit? For what, Ma?" I asked incredulously, looking up from the newspaper.

She frowned, showing disappointment, and said, "You don't know what's today? Beta, it's *Kushali* at the mosque!"

"So what? I am not going, Ma," I asserted, returning to my paper.

"Not going, eh?" she said. Her voice assumed the motherly tone of authority.

"I am going to Oyster Bay, Ma. I always go to Oyster Bay on Sundays. And today is Sunday."

"Oyster Bay? But... today is *Kushali!*" she exclaimed.

"So what?" I replied curtly, again returning to the newspaper, averting her gaze.

It was a blunt response, a provocation for her verbal tirade. And before long, the familiar sound of the wrathful words spewed from her thin mouth. I had heard them before directed at my father and my elder brother, Amin.

"*Haram zade! Mshenzi, Huna adabu weh*! Don't you have any shame talking to me like that, eh?" she said angrily.

"Don't you know today is a big day at the mosque? There is this important *farman* from *imam*. The whole community has been waiting for this news. And you want to go to Osster Bay at *mugrab* time?"

I continued reading the paper, avoiding any eye contact with her. The front page dominated with boisterous and victorious stories of liberation movements in South Africa: "Rebels Bomb Police Station: 4 *Boer* Policemen Killed."

Suddenly, her flour-covered right-hand reached across the dining table and ripped the newspaper from my hands.

Startled, I lurched back from my chair and looked at the towering body across the table. Her face was flushed and her brow covered with sweat from the kitchen heat; her eyes were wide open with rage.

She rested her hands on the wooden edge of the table, pinning the ripped, crumpled newspaper. She could have slapped me; my face was only her arms reach across the table.

"You look at me when I talk to you!" she demanded menacingly.

"You want to be an infidel, a Satan like your father and your brother, eh? They both are a disgrace to my family. Look at your father, a drunkard he is. All he does is drink at *mugrab* time with his friends. When was the last time your father came to the mosque with me, eh? Tell me. Tell me, eh?" She prompted me for an answer.

Her frantic tirade continued for a while. Now and then, her authoritative voice quivered. Sometimes, her large body trembled. I feared for her sanity.

So much pain she took on herself to maintain a certain idea of her faith which encompassed, in her mind, my father, my brothers and me, to be complete, to be realized. Faith for her was not a personal journey, but a collective one, one that had had to have us all as part of it. It was not her fault; it was what she had learned blindly, just like many others in the community for generations: first in India, now here in remote Africa.

"And your brother," she continued, placing the back of the palm of her left hand across her brow, and shaking her head in utter disgust, "*Budmas salo*, the whole *jamat* talks about him since he published that stupid book. And your father sells his books in our bookstore. My *nasib* to have son like him!"

"Ma. That book is a book of inquiry," I felt compelled to defend my brother, but then decided to remain quiet. Why fuel a raging fire?

My brother Amin had published a series of scathing newspaper articles about the legacy of our *imam* for a liberal leftist London newspaper, which were now expounded and published in book form. It had created quite a stir in the press in England. As a result, the *imam*, upon community outrage, had excommunicated him, and the repercussions of this act were fateful. It had affected our entire family; we were estranged from the community as well as from each other; and we lived under Amin's shadow. At school, I was taunted by my friends as *Satan's Brother*.

She had become irrational. I had never seen her so perturbed, so enraged. I reckoned her outbursts stemmed from deep fear of losing me, as I was coming of age. She had lost two sons: my brother Amin left home at a young age of eighteen — I was nine years old then — on a government scholarship to study in England; and younger to Amin, my other brother Shafiq, left home for Mozambique and joined the FRELIMO Liberation Army.

Losing her only remaining son to some African cause was unbearable for her. As it was, she was estranged from my father, who spent most of his time away from home, working at his small bookstore in the city center during the day and drinking with his friends at night. And when he returned, he would read into the early morning hours. Whenever I saw him on the way to the toilet, he would tell me, "I am acquiring knowledge…." He had given all three brothers his hunger for reading. Reading made him part of the larger world; he often felt he had missed on so much.

For Mother, I was her only hope; her life without me would be empty, except for the mosque and the going-ons in it. But that too was now increasingly difficult with Amin's communal banishment.

For many in our conspicuous community, the mosque — and the protected social and cultural life it offered — was the center of our limited universe. Many had not known (or bothered to know) any other life, any other culture, or any other people beyond the mosque boundaries. It was a "constructed" world — and a self-sustaining one.

She eyed me, frowning a little, as I stood up and walked briskly towards the bookshelf in the sitting room, passing the red stairway which led to our two bedrooms upstairs. From our glass bookshelf, I selected two books: *A Walk in the Night* by Alex La Guma and a book of poetry by Dennis

Brutus. I threw them inside my open *kikapu* that lay on the red sofa next to the bookshelf, grabbed it, and rushed for the front door, almost crashing into it.

She called out behind my back, "Haa, go away...go away. All of you go to hell. When I die, don't even come to my funeral..."

Then I heard soft sobs as I slammed the front door of the house behind me, and stepped out into the bright day. I briskly walked towards the Upanga Road, passing the length of identical, two-story communal flats where we lived.

On the door steps of the house at the end of the row of connected flats, sat an old, toothless, Indian woman, her face-shriveled and marked with age, her thick eye-lenses magnified her eyes, like two ping-pong balls behind a small frame.

She studied me, and called out, in Gujarati, "Aye Milibai's *chokra*. When you go to the mosque today, pray for Milibai." Then she spat beetle-juice, wiping the trickle from her jaw with her red frayed *patchedi*.

That is all she ever said to me each time our eyes met. Milibai was my deceased grandmother, and her childhood friend in Zanzibar.

I had loved my grandmother, and through her, I met her friend, Remtibai. Together, they would tell me about their father's India, so remote and distant and improbable in this African landscape, yet we were so inextricably bound to it. With the death of each generation, bits of that India faded, bits of the uncaptured history — their early struggles, fears in this new adopted land — perished, replaced by bits of new conflicting, confusing, and changing Africa.

"Yes, *Dadima*. I will pray for both of you."

Memories of my grandmother swelled inside me. My eyes became moist with unshed tears; I kept walking towards Oyster Bay, hoping that the gentle, cool, Indian Ocean breeze along the way would soothe me.

Along the way, I thought about Amin's writings: he had blatantly chided the community and some of its leaders as charlatans, and accused them of siphoning the country's treasures abroad. *"Over time"*, he wrote, *"the communal shell had hardened, entrapping its inhabitants with its ancient customs (and prejudice), blinding their vision. With its parochial schools and social institutions, with its unrelenting loyalty to their own kind in the independent African country, so rich and full of promise, they failed to make a difference. Instead, they profited. And now, they are deservedly paying for it."*

Unlike many others, he had cracked the cocoon, he had crossed the mosque boundaries, and he had become an insider looking from the outside, and found the core deformed with mass ignorance — a collection of uncultivated sensibilities.

So much rage (and self-hatred) permeated his writings. Was I being influenced by his embittered discourse? Or was I, like him, gradually looking from the outside and seeing the deformity?

I thought: "I mustn't let my brother's writings affect me. I must learn to look at the world my way, understand people through their history, their heritage and how their personal journeys, their struggles made them who they are today."

With that resolution, I kept on walking towards Oyster Bay, my gateway to a world beyond the confining boundaries of the mosque, where other peoples' history and inheritance will furnish a new vista into the human landscape.

Freedom Fighter

Part II

An official-looking man, dressed in pressed slacks and a white cotton shirt, walked through the open glass doors of our bookstore behind Samora Michel Avenue in town one Saturday morning and asked for my father.

The man was of mixed race. If we were in South Africa, he would be classified as "colored." His hair was wavy and curly with soft kinky loops, gray above the side burns; his exposed brown skin on his arms below the sleeves was taut and hairless, his muscles toned and fibrous. He had a graceful gait and posh mannerisms that carried an air of assumed superiority.

After spotting me behind the glass counter, he approached me and asked in accented English, "I am looking for Mr. Suleiman Budhani."

I reckoned he was a foreign books salesman, Cuban perhaps, from his accent. Dad was at the far end of the store, sorting and shelving books, when he heard me summon him.

"I am Eduardo De Silva from the FRELIMO," the man introduced himself, firmly shaking my father's hand.

"And you must be Jamil," the man said, giving a warm smile.

He looked around our disheveled bookstore and said, "Can we please sit down somewhere?"

Eduardo's assumed soothing voice belied an ominous portent. An official from the FRELIMO Liberation movement at our doorstep only suggested grave news.

My brother, Shafiq, had fled home three years ago and had traveled south; he wrote few letters home; and the last one informed us of his decision to join the liberation movement. Then silence for all this while. And now a personal message.

Dad led him to the makeshift office around one of the book shelves, and asked me to shut the store and join them in the back.

Eduardo placed an arm around my dad and said with echo of deep sorrow and sympathy in his voice: "Mr. Budhani, I have sad news for you. Your son, Shafiq, died, along with few of his comrades, in an ambush outside Laurenco Marques last week. We are profoundly sorry for your loss."

He gave us a few moments of silence to take in the news, and then hugged Dad and me, just as a close member of the family would, and told us woefully, "Your loss is not any different from the movement's. We all are a family, and we all ache from the tragic deaths of our beloved comrades. But the struggle must go on. We should not lose sight of the cause. We must reclaim what was always ours, what was denied and taken from us.

"Many like Shafiq will die; they will sacrifice their precious lives for the movement, so that future generations can enjoy the freedom and liberty denied them that we enjoy in this country.

"Shafiq believed in the human cause, even though he was not from Mozambique. But his principles were universal.

And I am honored to have met his family who instilled in him the compassionate values of human dignity, freedom and justice."

Dad broke down, and I swelled inside with waves of mixed emotion — confusion and anger. But anger for what? I thought.

Eduardo gestured at me to fetch a glass of water for Dad while he comforted him. When I returned, Dad had gathered himself, and was asking questions — in Portuguese — as he wiped his tears using the back of his palms, swiping across the cheeks.

"We managed to get the body, with the others as well. But we cannot bring it here. We simply do not have the means. I understand and respect your communal rites," Eduardo said, and then continued, "But we would like — with your permission and your presence — to hold a collective service for those who perished in the ambush."

"Where?" Dad asked.

"At one of our camps, at an undisclosed location, I hope you understand the secrecy. However, arrangements can be made for at most, two people, to attend. The drive will take a day, maybe more, weather and road conditions permitting. For security, we have to travel at night, and during the day, you may be asked to wear a hood."

He paused, his tolerant eyes studying our reactions, and when satisfied that we were not opposed to his conditions, continued in monotone voice, his words measured.

"Our leaders request that you attend, if at all possible. There is a supply truck leaving tonight and it will return Monday night. The service will be held tomorrow in the afternoon."

I thought, "Liberation movements have many aspects and fronts. Not all fight with arms; others do so with words. Eduardo was the public facing freedom fighter; Shafiq and others were the foot soldiers. The likes of Eduardo, with their grace and intellect, would appear on flashing screens of the Western media as spokespeople of the Liberation Fronts, with biting words, justifying their armed struggle. But with us, he showed another aspect of his sublime personality."

I had seen and read of Eduardo in the press. I had heard him along with Karim Shivji on the evening radio broadcasts. He would speak a few introductory statements in English, along with Karim Shivji, and switch to Portuguese for his target audience. And one sensed the fiery rage in his broadcast.

Dad studied me while I had my gaze fixed on Eduardo and said, "Yes. Jamil and I will attend."

"We will be honored to have you at the camp for the services. Resolution is the first step in the grieving process, painful as it is. But it is important," Eduardo said, placing his arm on Dad's shoulders.

"Pack a small bag, enough for couple of days. A man will identify himself tonight at 7:30 PM outside your bookstore. I am sorry but both of you will have to wear a hood to a location from where the supply truck will depart. The truck has canvas covers, so the hoods won't be necessary during the drive at night," Eduardo assured us.

After few seconds, Eduardo said, "I have taken your precious time, Mr. Budhani. You and your family perhaps want some private moments. I will leave now, and again, my deep condolences on our loss."

"Our" loss Eduardo had said. We were inexplicably linked to the larger movement. Shafiq, the freedom fighter, made that intangible link three years ago in a letter declaring his intentions to join the FRELIMO Liberation Movement.

Eduardo bid farewell and walked out (just as he had earlier walked in) into the golden sunlight. And between the span of those two events — his entry and exit through the swinging glass doors of our bookstore — our world was completely altered.

I lost a brother, and my parents a beloved son, the country a loyal citizen, but we also acquired, according to Eduardo, a large, extended family of faceless people, all fighting, some unwittingly, in their own ways, for a common cause, with their own idea of the movement, in formless landscapes deep in the African bush.

I thought, "How is Ma going to take this? Should we even tell her? For her Shafiq had gone away. I knew she still loved him, though she spoke bitterly of him, yet she yearned for that one day when he would come to his senses and return."

Just then, Dad looked up, his face solemn and sunken. As if reading my thoughts, he said in a broken voice: "Your mother mustn't know about Shafiq. We will tell her we are going to the interior for a couple of days to investigate a business opportunity.

"We both have to put up brave faces. It won't be easy. Eduardo was not clear on the state of the body. There was some sort of bomb blast. We shall find out when we get there, wherever that is."

Dad circled around the counter with the cash register on it and retrieved a hidden bottle of whiskey from underneath the counter and poured himself a stiff shot. For the rest of the afternoon, he ruefully drank and silently worked; now and then, I heard soft, muffled sobs of sorrow from his corner of comfort.

At seven thirty in the evening, an African man in nondescript civilian clothes approached us outside our dimly-lit bookstore. Our bookstore was located at the end of a series of small shops with large glass windows, in a thoroughfare between Samora

Michel Avenue and a small narrow street facing the cinema parking lot, across from the harbor.

He introduced himself as Roberto. He spoke our language, Kiswahili, with an accent, like many from the southern part of the country did.

Roberto's facial markings revealed his tribe: Makonde from Mozambique. I knew of the markings as passage rites to manhood. An old watchman — a refugee who had fled from the war-torn Mozambique and worked as a residential watchman where we lived in Upanga — had told me of it.

Roberto told us he was our escort, and he led us to a Land Rover parked around the corner. We dutifully followed in silence.

The evening crowd for the cinema, on the far side of the street, hurried to their destinations along the potholed narrow street, illuminated by the tall arching silver grimy lamps with elongated yellow fading bulbs; insects and small butterflies fluttered around it.

Always at this time of the evening in Dar, anywhere close to the Indian Ocean, a briny smell blended with humidity suspended in the air.

As we approached the car, another African man opened the back door for us, and smiling, handed us two black hoods. He asked politely to put them on.

The hoods were soft from many washes and made of cotton. Only a small mouth and nose piece were cut out; it fitted loosely on me. Immediately, the street light and everything around me disappeared, like a power outage, and darkness engulfed me; now and then the headlights of an oncoming vehicle formed an illuminated image of dispersed and formless patch of light.

I could hear Dad's heavy breathing. We depended on our audio senses.

The other African man assured us it will be a short ride. We drove for over half an hour, first through what sounded like the cacophony of the familiar city — noise from the evening traffic, Hindi songs from open Indian cafes, and audible human chatter from the busy street.

Then noise of the bustling city faded as we drove faster on a tarmac road; and eventually, we turned somewhere off the main road onto a bumpy one, which slowed us down as the Land Rover circumvented what may have been large potholes or depressions on the dirt road.

After a short drive, the Land Rover stopped. Outside, I heard human voices in Portuguese and Kiswahili, and a creaking noise from rising of a rusty sentry gate.

Roberto said, "Okay, we are here. You can take off the hoods, but hold onto them. You will need them tomorrow. Over there are the toilets if you want to relieve yourself. We have a long drive ahead of us."

Around us were a dozen low, white brick living quarters with barred windows and corrugated iron roofs. Inside a few of them, light from kerosene lantern flickered, casting giant shadows of people in the room on the walls; outside, naked bulbs illuminated the patchy grass on the ground.

Where we stopped was an administrative office. It was well lit inside. From the window, I could make out desks and chairs and bookshelves. At the end of the building was the kitchen with an open door, where two men in civilian clothes were loading two trucks with sealed cartoons and boxes.

Dad looked at me and his sullen expression asked me: *Did Shafiq come here first before going to where we are going tonight? Was this where his fateful journey began?*

Nothing of the place suggested of guerilla training camp — no armory, no warfare training grounds, no shooting ranges, but then it was a moonless night and nothing within fifty yards was clearly visible. It was perhaps a logistical center, tucked away on the outskirts of Dar, yet its secrecy was important to the movement.

As before, Roberto led us to the two camouflaged trucks with canvas tarp coverings. He stopped at the back of the second truck and opened its flopping canvas flap, and asked us to get in.

"Others will join us in minutes and we will depart," he informed us.

Inside the truck along both sides were upright benches. On the truck bedding laid sealed boxes of supplies: canned food, toiletries, and blankets; other wooden cartons were sealed without labels: perhaps ammunition.

Within minutes, we heard human voices outside our truck. Roberto opened the flap again, and a dozen men — all in army fatigues and boots and tipped caps — boarded. Each came to us and expressed their condolences; they knew who we were. Such a display of fellowship and camaraderie from strangers was heartening.

Roberto jumped in, and seconds later, the engines from both trucks fired and we set off to an undisclosed location into the vast African interior.

Roberto seemed like the leader of this convoy. Standing tall, he addressed them in Portuguese, and in unison, they all replied in monosyllable affirmations. After the routine, he came and sat next to us.

The faint light from a small naked bulb attached to the roof of the truck outlined the men's hardened faces, some marked by the ravages of time, others by tribal loyalties, and others still smooth, untouched, and innocent; their eyes were focused and full of resolve and eagerness.

From their mannerisms and response to Roberto's commands, they appeared as new recruits of the movement

from somewhere enroute to the "bush war." I had had heard
of liberation training camps somewhere in Morogoro, a
pastoral town west of Dar. Perhaps they were trained by
the African National Congress (ANC), the liberation front
fighting the apartheid regime in South Africa.

We drove for six hours on a smooth tarmac road. Dad
dozed off, fatigued from drinking in the afternoon and
drained from wrestling his emotions of the day. The
uncomfortable upright position did not faze or deny him
of sleep. Nor were the recruits denied rest. Perhaps part of
their training was to obtain sleep in any adverse conditions;
perhaps they were trained to control their minds, to shut
down when desired. Fighting a bush war or preparing for an
ambush often entails waiting and, sometimes, sleeping, in
far worse conditions than a moving truck with benches.

But I was alert, absorbing the experience, imagining
the lives of recruits before me, peacefully asleep, shoulder
to shoulder, wondering of their personal stories, of their
journeys from their villages to the city (and finally to
the camp), of their beloved ones left behind, and of their
motivation to join the movement. What was their idea of the
movement? *How was it different from Shafiq's?* I wondered.

Was the idea of joining the movement for them to liberate
the land of their ancestors from the colonial masters any
different than that of the Mau-Mau fighters in Kenya? Did
they embrace the fiery oratory of Karim Shivji on radio
FRELIMO espousing Marxist ideology?

Were their families supportive and proud? Would
Eduardo stop by one fateful day on their family household
doorstep and inform them of their beloved son's death, as
he did with us?

All of it was a journey of inquiry for me into the freedom fighter's personal motivation as much as it was to bury them.

The truck changed into low gears often, as if strenuously climbing steep hills. Traffic noise from convoys of passing vehicles broke the monotone drone of our trucks. These convoys of semi-trucks driven by Somali drivers carried long bars of rusty, crimson copper from Zambia on their open beds, stacked up and secured with steel cables, enroute to the coastal city we left (when Portuguese colonizers of Mozambique went to war with the rebels, Zambia could no longer use the port Laurenco Marques for its exports).

It was an indication that we were traveling south, going up country towards the border, closer to Mozambique.

At some point during the night both trucks pulled up on the side of the road. Roberto addressed his squad in Portuguese before instructing us that we were stopping for a short break to relieve ourselves. The bush is your toilet, he told everyone jokingly, but do not drift too far into it, otherwise the hyenas may surprise you.

Outside, pitch darkness engulfed us, cut by beams of flashlights crisscrossing, as the recruits meandered towards the low shrubbery. Shortly, a convoy of semi-trucks, on its way to fetch its cargo of copper, passed us, its searching and powerful headlights revealing the long stretch of road ahead.

Then darkness again, only pools of illumination from each truck's red parking lights revealed the small area of the tarmac. The fluttering sounds of buzzing insects, attracted to the truck's parking lights, and incessant sounds of chirping crickets from the deep jungle, pierced the quiet night. The air felt cool on the exposed skin.

Above us the moonless sky appeared very low, like an oversized blanket, stretching for miles, dotted with large luminous sparkling stars in their marked constellations.

From what little I saw and heard and smelled around me — the cool, damp air, the dense vegetation, and the copper trucks — I had some idea of where we were: deep in the interior of the high country, heading south, perhaps towards Mikandani or Mtwara region, closer to the Mozambique border, across from the majestic Ruvuma River.

After some time, Roberto called out and all the recruits gathered and boarded the truck. Dad never alighted; when we first stopped he woke, mumbled, and went back to sleep, only this time, he slumped on the hard truck bed, using our small hand luggage to support his head, and leaned against the supplies of boxes.

We resumed our journey, sometimes climbing; sometimes going downhill, traversing what seemed like the southern high country of the Makonde plateau.

Roberto turned off the only light on the roof of the truck, and unfurled a few inches of the tarp to let in fresh cool air, releasing the trapped warm air inside, mixed with body odor and smell of ripe fruits in the boxes.

The once-hardened faces of recruits seemed peaceful and serene in their sleep. I let darkness consume me and comfort my tiring body.

When I woke it was bright outside. Streams of golden light flooded inside the truck at an angle from the raised and rolled up tarp. Everybody around me was awake. The truck had turned onto a bumpy dirt rutted road, moving slowly, circumventing wide troughs left over from the rainy season.

Outside, on either sides of the dirt road, was scant vegetation of the coastal forest: low shrubs, uncultivated wild grasses, trees with scant foliage, and a few coconut trees now and then. We were around the southern coastline.

We had traveled over twelve hours, stopped only once, and had eaten nothing. Just then, Roberto cracked open one of the carton boxes of wheat crackers which he passed to everybody. The recruits were sipping hot tea from their army tin mugs. Roberto handed me a tin mug of dark tea and a piece of bread.

Dad was awake, smiled and said: "I slept through it all."

"You needed it most," I said.

"We are only couple of hours away from the camp. It is 10:00 AM. We will be there by noon," Roberto announced, after consulting his army watch strapped on his wrist.

Now and then, Roberto talked into a large walkie-talkie whenever it crackled. It was a full-sized gadget, with extended antenna pointing outwards. I had seen such devices in war movies where embattled soldiers would shout into it amid enemy gunfire, seeking rescue and air cover. He must be in communication with his comrades in the other truck ahead of us, I reckoned.

My thoughts turned to Roberto. I wondered why he joined the revolutionary movement.

"How long have you been with the movement?" I asked.

Dad pretended as if he was disengaged but I knew he was interested as well in anything that would reveal Shafiq's journey, Shafiq's unaccounted time for the last three years: a patch of darkness for all of us.

Roberto studied me as if part of him wanted to reveal, yet, part of him shrank from the question. But my inquiries did not surprise him. I could tell someone before me had asked him, for his answers each time were well-formed, refined, and calibrated.

Roberto had an easy way about him. When he wanted, he could switch to another mode — that of a commanding officer — unlike the recruits, who seemed somber most of the time. Occasionally they would talk in Portuguese, smile a little, and then gaze out blankly at the receding dirt road.

"Five years," Roberto answered.

"What made you join the struggle?"

"Like my grandfather before him, my father worked and toiled in settler plantations all his life in Beira on land that belonged to our ancestors. But he was happy being enslaved. He knew nothing else. He followed what his father did, like a family trait passed to the next generation. We lived on the settler farm, in the servant quarters. It was the life I did not want to lead for myself and my progeny. I had a choice of following his footsteps, or breaking away. And that choice came my way one day.

"A well-spoken man appeared before me on my way to secondary school. He asked me to bring myself and a few classmates with him that evening to a secret location in the bush. He said it was best for young people to join the struggle to free themselves. Some of us started attending these secret gatherings in the bush late at night, in secrecy.

"There we met others, members of the FRELIMO Liberation Front. The man and his friends wore army fatigues and told us all about the struggle. They said they were part of the Mozambique Liberation Movement here to recruit the young workers and students from the settler farming communities' quarters.

"They returned to us our buried sense of dignity and pride. Unearthing my dignity and pride as an African is what FRELIMO did for me," said Roberto.

"What role do you play in the struggle?" I asked.

"The movement has numerous facets. I have many roles. And we are not at liberty to discuss our roles with fellow comrades, but there is always something for someone to do in the large scheme of things. Whatever little you do, it does contribute to the struggle," Roberto said, smiling.

Eduardo had alluded to multitudinous nature of the movement in Dar in the bookstore to us. Not everybody has to be a foot soldier, he had said. The movement is not all about armed struggle; it is a mental struggle of liberation as well.

It must be part of training to answer questions in certain way, when facing civilians or potential recruits.

I thought, "Roberto's motivation for joining the movement was different from Shafiq's. Shafiq's idea of the struggle lay elsewhere. Clearly not for liberation of any ancestral land, for we had no ancestral land in Africa to fight for. Some of us were descendants of migrant workers and traders, transported from one conquered territory — across the waters of the Indian Ocean — to another.

"Our family history in Africa was sketchy and vague, unchronicled, and some would accuse my people of exploitation. Was Shafiq liberating himself from that stigma? Was fighting for an African cause an act of redemption?"

The trucks slowed down and finally stopped, with the engines still running. Outside, we heard welcoming human voices, perhaps sentries. The truck moved again. From the open flap, I saw a high, meshed fence with barbed wires and a gate. On either side of the gates were tall sentry towers with armed guards on the lookout.

We finally came to a stop. Roberto stood up and said something to the recruits and turned to us and said, "We are at the camp. There is no need to wear your hoods. Please do not ask questions to any of the comrades about our destination or about their journey. Even they don't know where we are."

Portuguese speaking Africans — in fatigues and tipped caps and army boots — welcomed us as we alighted from the truck. Some uniformed men unloaded the supplies, while the recruits formed two lines, and marched off to an open field behind and around a central large army tent, commanded by another officer.

All around us were large olive and camouflaged tents, with open triangular flaps, evenly spaced in the middle of a clearing as large as a football pitch. The camp area was enclosed by ten-foot-tall barbed wire fence with sentry towers. Beyond the perimeter was the bush: low, thorny shrubbery, sparse trees with convoluted branches and thin foliage, and endless golden grass, swaying slightly in the wind.

The only low cement building in the middle of the clearing with corrugated iron roof and windows along its length faced us. It was a dispensary.

A couple of green army trucks with large wheels and a jeep were parked beside each tent. In the center of the camp, across from the hospital, was a circular dirt mound, encircled with white bleached stones. From the center of the mound, a flag post hoisted a Tanzanian flag, dangling on this windless afternoon.

This must be it, I thought; it was the FRELIMO training ground disguised as a Tanzanian army barracks. It had all the facilities of the barracks: the army vehicles, the dispensary, the sleeping tents, mess halls inside the tents, and at far end of the camp, away from the camp ground facilities, were guerilla training grounds and firing ranges.

Roberto approached us with another solemn-looking African, smooth-faced and with a fringe of curling gray hair, dressed in army fatigues under his white medical robe.

"This is Comrade Joachim, one of our doctors at the camp. He will take you to the dispensary where other relatives of our comrades are waiting," Roberto introduced us.

Joachim smiled and gestured as he guided us towards the dispensary.

He said, "We will start the service as soon as our guest, Comrade Michel Samora, arrives."

"Samora Michel is going to attend the service?" Dad asked excitedly.

"Yes, he does most of the time, when a few comrades die in action. He lost one of his relatives as well," said Joachim.

The inside of the building looked like a rural health clinic with white glossy painted walls. The sterile scent from the medicine filled the air. Few white-clothed staff — freedom fighters of a different kind — hurried up and down the corridor. Some were women but their tipped caps, tucked hair, hardened faces, and white robes over army fatigues and boots erased their femininity.

Joachim led us to a quiet room, comfortably furnished with sofas and chairs — even here, in the deep interior, amidst the training grounds of combat, the notion of a waiting room was preserved. It was occupied by a dozen other people, mainly African and an Asian Goan-looking couple. They all looked up and nodded, their misty eyes and withdrawn faces showed grief.

"Do you wish to pay your last respects?" asked Joachim.
Dad nodded.

"But I have to warn you that the condition of the body may upset you. You have to be strong. A blast does damage limbs and tissues," Joachim added in the controlled voice of a comforting physician.

Dad nodded again, bravely. He looked at me asking if I wanted to come along.

I nodded.

Joachim led us through the closed door inside the waiting room into another area of the building and down a narrow corridor. At the end, he opened a metal door of what seemed like a makeshift morgue kept at a low temperature by the generator.

In the center of the room was a large table with metal top. On it laid twenty bodies covered in white cloth and next to each body a large slab of ice. The slabs of ice and the generator kept the room at a low temperature. There was a slight stench of dead flesh in the room and a deadly, eerie silence.

Joachim led us to the center of the table and gently (but partially) raised the white sheet with a tag labeled "Shafique" pinned to it.

I had not seen Shafiq for three years. He left with us the image of him with long hair, scruffy beard, youth — and boundless idealism. His idea of the movement had rendered him to a ghastly cadaver.

He had no hair and no beard and only thin eyebrows above sunken sockets; his face was bloated and purplish-black, and stains of dried blood, in splotches, covered his neck and upper chest. One hand was torn off; a stump from the shoulder was wrapped in cotton bandage, which was stained from dried blood; what else was maimed underneath white sheet, we wished not to see. From the way the white sheet outlined the rest of his body, it appeared one leg was partially missing.

The stench was overwhelming now with the partially uncovered body, and I became sick and retched at the nearby bin.

Dad went to his old ways of faith: he recited prayers, just as people did at our mosque over a dead face before the *mukhi,* asking for redemption and forgiveness. Then he kissed Shafiq's forehead gently and moved back, teary eyed, shaking with silent and controlled sobs, and gestured to Joachim, who covered the body and led us gently outside where he gave us some fizzy drinks to subside the nausea.

Shortly after, we joined the rest of the grieving families in the waiting room. Dad derived solace from his little flask of whiskey; it gave him temporary comfort.

Every time I thought of Shafiq in the makeshift morgue, I had to run to the bathroom, my stomach queasy, my knees wobbly, but I shed no tears of sorrow, only felt numbness.

When I returned, I asked Dad, "Are they going bury Shafiq here?"

"Yes, with the others, Joachim told me. How can we take him back like this? He wanted to be part of this, he gave his life; he belongs here with the rest," said Dad.

"Are you going to tell Ma?" I asked.

Dad pondered for while and without looking at me said, "When the time is right."

Outside, rumbling noise from a descending helicopter distracted us. I looked out through the barred window. The helicopter, with the markings of the Tanzanian army, gently landed in the middle of the clearing, its rotating blades swirling up dust from under low, dried grass. A number of officers ran, dodging slightly, towards its doors to receive the arriving party.

When the doors opened, a young, light-skinned uniformed army officer alighted down the steps, followed by Comrade Samora Michel, dressed in his fatigues, boots, tipped cap, and a revolver strapped to his waist, like Fidel Castro. He shook hands with everyone on the ground, spoke with Joachim and others from the receiving party. Then the young uniformed officer, Joachim, and Samora Michel strode towards the hospital.

The doors of our waiting room swung open and there before us was Samora Michel, the elusive leader of the armed struggle, the most wanted man across the Ruvuma River; his iconic images — of the power fist and victory sign — marked our daily papers. He seemed a small and compact man, with searching, intelligent eyes. The scruffy goatee completed the image of the past revolutionaries: Trotsky, Lenin, Che, and Castro.

He addressed us all in the room, speaking softly and measurably, his voice deep.

"My heart weeps, just as yours does today. But this is not the end. Some of our brothers and sisters, who live in servitude under the colonial masters of Europe, have to die first so others can live in dignity. Your sons and daughters were exceptional fighters, not only on the field but in their minds. It was their liberating minds that put them forward, propelled them, and furnished them with the strength to fight.

"A freedom fighter, first and foremost, has to liberate mentally, unshackle the servile mentality. He has to erase his past, create a new identity, a vision of himself as truly in control of his life and his destiny. Our comrades transformed themselves and led by example.

"And I am as much proud of them as you all are. But fellow comrades, freedom will come to us, slowly and painfully and with immense loss, but those who sacrificed shall never be forgotten.

"We are gathered here not say farewell to the dead, for they are not dead. They always will be alive, just as our ancestors are in the occupied land. The spirit of an African revolutionary is an infinite spectrum. It will always exist.

"I am here on behalf of the movement, on behalf of the enslaved people, and I carry the burden of your sorrow with me every living moment of my breath."

Then, he paused after that last statement, and with unexpected high voice exclaimed: "Viva FRELIMO! Viva Mozambique!" giving his trade mark fist of black power salute.

And instinctively, we all responded in kind.

"Viva FRELIMO! Viva Mozambique!"

The room elated in jarring applause, and for a moment, it seemed that I was at a political rally rather than a funeral service. In my mind's eye, images of a political rally I had attended with Shafiq at the Hill, University of Dar — when Fidel Castro gave a three-hour, uninterrupted rousing speech, translated in tandem to a standing room auditorium of enthusiastic students — played like a short film. Every detail was vivid, as though I was transformed back in time, three years ago. And Shafiq would look down at me, smiling, nodding, and beaming with elation, afloat in the rapture of the moment.

I thought as I watched and admired the leader before me: *That must have been the turning point in Shafiq's life.*

After his short delivery of what seemed like a service eulogy, Samora Michel greeted every family personally, talking softly to them, placing his right arm around the weeping mothers, the delicate tender touch of a trained nurse. And he finally came to us, flanked by the light skinned uniformed officer from the helicopter — she was of mixed race and well-spoken — who translated for me all he said.

Dad and I met and shook hands with of one of the most powerful and wanted man in the African southern hemisphere, the man responsible to head the armed struggle with all its justified casual brutalities, yet he did not convey that power, that menace, that rage.

Samora Michel's presence was soothing and comforting and he drew me into his bosom of comfort. All his training as a nurse — like Che's as a medical student — gave him the human, soft touch of tenderness, and yet when required to inspire comrades to pick up arms for the cause, he could transform himself into the fiery orator of Marxist revolutionary ideology.

All the while as Samora spoke, I never thought of the make-shift morgue: the maimed bodies in there, the consequences of the armed struggle. His presence fleetingly erased it from thoughts, and Dad nodded in affirmation, like the other parents in the room, acknowledging what was being said.

Dad was born and raised in Mozambique, spoke Portuguese, and had moved up north to Tanzania later in life to seek business opportunities. Mozambique was his first home, Tanzania his adopted country, and before that, all is a void. Little I knew of my grandfather's past, only sketchy details of their migration from South Africa up north. All links back to India were lost and severed.

When Samora Michel finished his rounds of the grieving parents, Joachim instructed us all to gather outside the infirmary, where a truck was parked. They had loaded the coffins — make-shift cardboard boxes like the ones we saw in photographs of the African National Congress (ANC) martyrs being buried in near Soweto — in the open military truck. We all walked behind the funeral truck as it slowly edged along a dirt road heading towards the far end of one side of the camp.

The funeral procession was headed by the leading members — Joachim, Samora Michel, and other senior officers from the camp; they sang familiar hymns, the ones I heard repeatedly in Dar, in the evening's FREMLIMO and ANC radio broadcasts.

Behind us, the rest of the recruits from the camp had joined the procession, forming a lengthy line, like a human snake, as it meandered along the dirt road, with the truck as the snake's head.

We stopped at the edge of the dirt road. A narrow, grassy pathway led to rows of twenty dug-out, open graves. All around it were rows of graves, with boards as tombstones, announcing the comrades who had perished for the cause.

High above us, in the afternoon cloudless blue sky, African vultures glided effortlessly in circles, hovering, waiting, as if when the crowd disappears, what lay beneath the graves would be dug up and devoured by them.

A number of designated guerillas carried the coffins and asked respective families to help carry them. Dad and I shouldered, on each side, Shafiq's coffin, its sharp edge cutting deep into my flesh. And as pallbearers — just as we did at our mosque, carrying the dead — we led him to his resting place.

In moments of profound suffering, when nothing else provides solace, one falls back into the old ways of faith. Dad broke into the Muslim hymns I had heard often outside our mosque during a funeral procession, when the crowd carried the coffin, wrapped in chintzy cloth, on their shoulders, passing from one pallbearer — young and old, with the family members always in the middle — to another, like an army of ants carrying a large piece of dead flesh to its destination.

Each family, with the help of the comrades, lowered the coffin into the grave with sisal ropes. Momentarily, twenty gunshots, one for each martyr, broke the silence, startling me, as the movement collectively paid their tribute to their lost brethren. After the gunshots, more songs of freedom followed.

I had broken out in a sweat, and Dad was perspiring. His tears were washed away by rivulets of sweat trickling down his face from the hard labor of covering Shafiq's cardboard coffin with the mounds of dirt from the dug-up grave.

After the burial, Dad stood up, gestured for me to stand next to him, and said his Muslim prayers; I tried to follow. The other families recited their Catholic prayers; their sons may have been Marxists (and atheists) but their families were steeped in the colonial faith of the rulers.

When we returned to the waiting room, they were serving snacks — biscuits, refreshments, some meat cutlets — from the supplies truck that had brought us from Dar and shortly would take us back.

Some members of the families were boarding a truck which was going to take them back. Where to? I wondered. They could not have come from across the border: all traffic and communication between Tanzania and Mozambique had ceased; we were the front-line state – and at a proxy war with our southern neighbor.

The female translator — Ana Bella was her name, she said gracefully when she met us along with Samora Michel — was talking with families and other uniformed men in the waiting room. Her fine physique was concealed under the army fatigues, and her hair was tucked inside the tipped cap with a red star. From where I stood, close to the door, I could see the muscles of her delicate, long neck twitch as she spoke. One of her eyes was slightly crossed so when she looked at you while talking, her deep-set green eyes above her high cheek bones gave her a seductively intelligent look. When flanked by Samora Michel she was at least six inches taller than he.

As I gazed at her, I thought she was of mixed race and one of her parents must be a European, perhaps a colonial Portuguese, living in an estate. Was she the result of the late night liaisons between the master and the female African servants in their quarters?

What part of her heritage motivated her to join the movement? Was her idea of the armed struggle the rejection of her European heritage? Was she ashamed of her European heritage — and its legacy on the continent — so much so that now she fought against them?

Her mannerisms and speech indicated refined education. She could not have grown up in the servant quarters to be schooled at the mediocre schools aimed at producing a generation of servants. She must have studied abroad or in one of the exclusive European schools in the Laurenco Marques meant for the colonials where she might have been subjected to racial taunts aimed at her mixed race.

Her personal history, like that of Roberto, was intriguing to me — how she came to be what she is today, her transformation. So I mustered enough courage to approach Ana Bella and introduced myself. I remembered being instructed by Roberto not to ask questions of comrades at the camp, but Roberto was nowhere in sight, and she was forthcoming when I spoke to her.

She told me she had never met "Shafique" but was truly sorry for us.

I nodded.

"Do you travel a lot with Samora Michel?" I asked.

"Comrade Samora Michel," she corrected me, smiling.

"Yes. I am the official translator. I attend meetings with him when we have to meet our foreign dignitaries in support of the armed struggle. I can speak French, Spanish, Portuguese, and English and I picked up Russian along the way. I studied foreign languages at the university," she said.

"That is very impressive and admirable. Where did you do your studies?

"Imperial College, London," she said.

"Did you like London?" I asked.

"Not as a place to live, but I enjoyed studying there. It is a historical city; its old architecture speaks of history. The Londoners do not see it that way, but outsiders, curious ones who look hard, discover far more than what meets the eye — the legacy of the British Empire, the brutality of the class system, concealed behind the pediments, the columns and the grandeur facades, museums, clubs. The locals have to dig for them. Outsiders with an acute eye see them," she said, looking down at me, with those deep green eyes, one slightly off to the left.

"Is that different from Lisbon, the history, I mean?" I asked

She studied me before answering, "No. At the end of the day, the capital served as the head of the empire. From those grand buildings, it ruled a distant place."

"What motivated you join the armed struggle? Was it personal or political?" I ashamedly blurted out.

Again, she paused; her green eyes regarded my probing question.

I felt she had sensed I had seen through her, and she asked curtly, "Why do you think Shafique joined the liberation front?"

"I don't know. I never had a chance to ask him. But I think I have an idea," I replied.

"And what is that?"

"Something inside Shafiq carried a burden of his race. He wanted acceptance. I think it was misguided, sentimental."

"I see," she said, and then looking out the open door, as if contemplating whether to dismiss my remarks or respond, and added, "I think that is rather simplistic and judgmental. It is a bit complicated. True, that people are moved by personal and political convictions, but race has nothing to do with it. The conviction derives from a strong sense of justice. Over time you too will realize. Shafique did not die in vain.

"You are upset, and I understand," she said conveying immense empathy with her green eyes, looking down upon me.

Her towering body leaned forward, and she tenderly kissed me on both my cheeks. Her soft lips felt warm against my cheeks. That gesture of tenderness stirred and uncoiled a stubborn knot of emotions inside me. Everything I had held back from the Saturday morning when Eduardo visited us — or my incapacity to mourn or cry — poured out in violent sobs. She held my trembling body in a sisterly embrace.

At that point, Roberto walked in, looking for us.

She said something to Roberto in Portuguese, and Roberto led me back to the truck, guiding me by my shoulders.

Dad was busy chatting with the Goan couple outside. I told Roberto I did not want my Dad to see me crying, so we went around the back.

Later, Dad told me about the Goan parents; they were political refugees from Mozambique living in Iringa. Like us, they had lost their son, who was older than Shafiq.

We departed shortly for the long drive back to Dar in the same truck. This time, instead of new recruits, we had a seasoned regiment, perhaps heading back for training others elsewhere; they seemed older and mature. The only familiar face was that of Roberto. There was enough room on the truck's rutted bed without the supplies that Dad and I could sleep on it.

Physically wearied and emotionally drained from the past two days' events, sleep came easily, drowning all the noise and steadying the motion of the truck. When we woke we were back where we had begun two days ago, at a small camp somewhere in Dar. Roberto asked us to put on our hoods and he dropped us off at our shop in town.

Dad suggested we get some breakfast at the A-Tea Shop, a famous place for kebabs and steaming hot Indian tea. We did not speak much; each of us had our own thoughts of the last two days. The only thing Dad said was, "I will tell Ma when the time is right, Jamil. No one else should know what happened, especially Shafiq's friends or your friends. You know how our community is. With what Amin did with his writing, it will just give them extra venom."

I nodded.

Over weeks and months, Dad slipped into his normal routine: work, drink, sleep, and back to work; he drank more than usual now, perhaps his way of dealing with his grief.

I resumed my last term of post-secondary education, at the Mzizima Secondary School, and finished it that year. I did not know what lay ahead of me. So much of my prospects depended on my grades.

One Saturday morning — like that Saturday morning seven months ago when Eduardo had walked into our lives and altered it forever — I came home from a game of football and heard wails of grief from our flat as I approached the courtyard. There were neighbors gathered outside the flat. Something terrible must have happened to Dad, I thought.

When I stepped inside, Mother was on the floor, screaming and banging her head against it, her forehead covered with blood, her hair wild and matted with blood, her eyes maddeningly red from crying.

She was screaming for Shafiq, her dead son.

"My boy is dead! Oh, my boy is dead! How could they do that to him?"

Dad was kneeling over her trembling body, trying to calm her. He had told her. He had found the right moment. But, clearly, it was not the right moment. Perhaps he should have waited longer.

Ma was inconsolable, and from that fateful day on, whatever was left of her sanity perished, and she went insane. Our family servant, Moosa, who had worked and lived with us for many years, regretfully returned to his village. He told us it was unbearable to see Ma. He said she had been possessed by the spirits and needed help.

Our quiet home had turned into an asylum. Dad refused to put her into the hospital. The conditions were atrocious, he said, so we fed her drugs and treated her with shock treatments at the Muhimbili Hospital.

Finally, the results of the examination were published in the Daily News. I had received distinction marks for all my subjects: history, economics, and mathematics. My application for a bursary to study abroad from our community was rejected, for reasons I knew, but the official letter stated scholarships were only for engineering and medicine and not liberal arts.

Thinking of Ana Bella one day — I saw her picture in the paper, without her army fatigues and tipped cap. She was dressed in western clothes, looking tall and elegant and stately, alongside Scandinavian dignitaries, flanked by smiling Samora Michel and Eduardo De Silva, in Oslo at a conference — I applied to Imperial College in London.

In my essay for the application to the college, I wrote that I aspired to be a writer, but I could not articulate what I wanted to write about, except that I was passionately interested in people's histories. After a few paragraphs, words and sentences failed me to carry on, so I abruptly ended the essay with a remark that it takes a lifetime of experiences to be a writer, to understand the world, to develop a vision, a voice, from which narratives emerge. And to know other worlds — and their people — I had to leave this confining world of Dar: the world that Oyster Bay provided me, constructed for me, was limiting in its social human depth.

Three months on, I received an admission and a partial bursary from the college. And soon, I left for London. Dad made arrangements with whatever savings we had left and bought the airfare. He assured me Ma will recover, and urged me to write every day, whatever I could. He encouraged me to write about our people in Africa; nobody does.

He said to me on my departing day, "Be a fighter in whatever you aspire to do in life, and with it will come victory and freedom."

What Eduardo had said, on that fateful Saturday, was that not everybody fights with weapons in the liberation movement. The movement is larger than that; it has many facets. One chooses the battle one wishes to fight, and one becomes *its* freedom fighter.

It all came to me now like illumination of what Roberto and Ana Bella had said to me about their personal motivation for joining the movement. I had misjudged Shafiq's motivations. His journey, like Ana Bella's, was personal and political. We all have our personal reasons to join a cause — out of conviction perhaps. His race was irrelevant, so was Ana Bella's.

My journey had begun and I was its new recruit; my liberation would come with the process of writing. The voice will unfold itself; the material will reveal itself. Until then I would be its freedom fighter — seeking and traversing peoples' historical landscapes for narratives.

Family Reunion

Extended and distant families, the ones you have never met but always hear about at dinner conversation or at other family gatherings, arouse a mixture of curiosity, unease and envy. Ours was a large extended family, dispersed across countries in southern Africa – Tanzania, Rhodesia, and South Africa.

We were the Dhamani family, and our history was preserved (and passed on to the next generation) with the oral tradition of storytelling. My grandmother heard narratives about her father's brothers, several of them, of their arduous journeys, along with other indentured workers from India, across the perilous Indian Ocean in rickety dhows. They first arrived along the coastal towns of East Africa in early 1800s; from there a few moved southwards to Maputo, Salisbury, and Durban. The details of the narrative were sketchy when narrated to me when I was a young boy; it seemed so simple; nothing of the hardship was ever narrated. Only who married into what family, what success it brought them, what failures wrought them, nothing more, all untraceable and unverifiable. It all could be just fiction. Nothing was ever chronicled.

It was this curiosity and unease that has stayed with me all my life. And even after reuniting with them one day in Salisbury, nothing came of it, no illumination, no connection to India; my distant cousins were as much in darkness as I was; their upbringing in their respective countries had cultivated in them a sense of identity with the continent; their idea of who they thought they were, after independence from the colonial masters, dissolved that false sense of security.

My grandmother's oral historical narratives did not give me anything. It was a charade, I thought. I had to discover for myself. And that day came when a courier from the south showed up with a message. The letter was written in Gujarati, and addressed to my grandmother in her maiden name, Gulbanu Shams Dhamani:

> *My Sweet Gulbanu Bhen,*
>
> *I am your cousin from Salisbury. Our fathers were brothers in India. I have a farm outside Salisbury now, and I have done well, thank God, and we the Dhamani family, all of us from South Africa and Rhodesia are meeting to reunite here after many years being apart. We all have been dispersed over the years, but we all here talk about your family up north and we all want to see your grandchildren.*
>
> *Nothing would please me more than that every Dhamani be present at the farm. We have a huge farm to accommodate everyone.*
>
> *The address of the farm is on the back side, and the date that everybody will be here is 22 December 1966.*

*May God give you and our family the good fortune
to be reunited again, even if it is for only a few days.*

Yours truly,

*Bhai Shamshoodin Jamal Dhamani.
1 November 1966*

So that is how it all started – the preparations for a
journey south – with a simple message of unity.

Our grandmother lived with us; she had lost my
grandfather, Jalaluddin Ismail Jamal, to lung cancer at an
early age, contracted from working in the coal mines. She
had survived selling cooking oil canisters from a room made
into a makeshift shop, in a dark alleyway in old Dar on a
street now called Nkrumah Street (then it was just a simple
dusty road with makeshift huts; destitute Indians and Arabs
slept on the asphalt).

Single-handedly, she raised my father and his two
sisters. Even during those extraordinary times, she was a
strong matriarch, not common in Indian households. Her
immigrant spirit of survival had carried her through the
hardships of Africa, her new land of birth, and through
the bitter battles of the extended family. But she never told
us much of her hardships; she suppressed most of it in her
stories. Her narratives were of only good times.

When my father arrived from work, Grandma demanded
that arrangements for the journey should commence, along
with all the other Dhamani clan in Dar. My mother did not
have any say in the matter; the matriarch of the family had
spoken, and her request was to be granted.

My dad worked for Kasamali and Hasanali Dhamani,
two of my grandmother's nephews, in a large cattle supply

farm and slaughterhouse, along with other less-fortunate Dhamani clan members. The Dhamani brothers had done well for themselves. They had begun as cattleherd's men in the interior, working alongside the Gogo tribesman, cattle and sheep herders of the Dodoma region, raising cattle and supplying them as carcasses to European-owned butcheries in the city. Over the years, some Europeans had left, handing ownership and the business to Dhamani brothers, who managed the enterprise and built a fortune. In turn, they employed all the less-fortunate Dhamani clan members; employing family members was not an uncommon practice among the Asians. You could trust family not to cheat on you. Well, not quite. Money and greed purges blood relations.

The Dhamani clans in Dar were a unit, an organization, self-sustaining. Its strength was its cohesiveness, as well as its weakness. It had intricate rules of communication and social behavioral hierarchy, preserved for generation from India, and now mixed with the African ways, as many among us took on Arab-African wives.

Dad said, "It is a long drive to Salisbury. Can you sit in the Land Rover for that long?"

Grandma replied, "No. I will go with Kasamali Dhamani. He will take his mini-bus. I can sleep in the back. But we must go. I want to meet all my cousins before I die."

Dad said, "Okay, I will talk to Kasamali or Hasanali bhai tomorrow."

Word from Dad the next day was that both Hasanali and Kasamali had received an identical invitation, and were planning on driving in the mini-bus, the vehicle used to ferry workers back and forth between the slaughterhouse and the butcheries in town.

Dad facetiously said to us that the bus would have to be scrubbed and washed thoroughly to carry family members; it reeked of dried blood and sweat. Sometimes it carried carcasses, wrapped in gunny sack with ice, and it was the stench from this fleshy cargo and the dripping blood from the carcasses' hind legs that embedded in the seats and the floor. On a hot day, with windows closed inside the mini-bus, the stench emerged, mixing with the hot trapped air and assaulted the senses.

Dad, Mom, Grandma, and my two younger brothers – Faisal and Jamil, several years younger than I – were exhilarated from the news of the long journey down south. It was the end of my fourth form.

Rarely did we, as a family, drive into the interior, though Dad often went there, in search of cattle from the African herdsmen, sometimes living among them for weeks. There were rumors among the Dhamani clan that Dad had taken on an African wife (and had children with her) in the village.

Once, I had seen a faded, black-and-white picture of Dad, draped around the waist in African loincloth, shirtless, seated in a hut, with an African woman tending to him and two young, half-naked children with half-Indian features, clinging onto him. The picture was carefully hidden inside Dad's cupboard, and I chanced upon it accidentally, looking for stashed-away cash. Then I did not think much of it. After all, several Dhamanis had taken on African and Arab wives; it was not uncommon within the clan; and others had Arab mistresses.

But Mother never talked about it, never talked about anything much. She had resigned herself to her fate, and led the life of the Dhamani clan member's wife: subservient to the husband, tended to the children, helped out in the business, kept the books in order, and ensured we received proper schooling at the parochial schools.

What other choice did she have? Her parents had warned her of the darker side of a large and extended family, its cruelty, but love had blinded caution and reason and parental wisdom.

Both Hasanali and Kasamali had planned and organized to depart Dar the early morning of December 18th. Two mini-buses and the Land Rover would comprise the convoy. The African drivers would drive the mini-buses, carrying all the Dhamani children, wives and men, and Dad would drive the Land Rover, carrying some of the African workers from the slaughterhouse and butchery.

The night before the departure none of us – Faisal, Jamil and I – could sleep. Excitement and wonder kept us awake. The idea of driving for days into the interior and crossing two other countries before reaching our destination marveled me. It was my first long distance overland trip. And it evoked inside me a distinct feeling of departure, going away to a faraway place. It was the opposite feeling of melancholy that gripped me whenever I went to the airport or the harbor with Dad to send off the well-to-do children of the Dhamanis overseas, their hands waving from the airplane's porthole or from the steamer's deck. The idea of departure made me feel abandoned.

We drove in Dad's Land Rover to meet with the rest of the convoy early morning, 4:30 AM, at Kasamali's bungalow in Msasani, past the Salendar Bridge. Both mini-buses were full of excitable children; women chatted inside the bus, while the men loaded the luggage and food, prepared by women from the previous night for the trip, into the back of

the truck. As always with Dhamani trips and picnics food —
large pots of curry, bread, rice, samosas and bajias, and large
thermoses of Indian tea — are central to the occasion.

Grandma and Mother and my two brothers joined the
rest on the mini-bus, but I chose to ride with Dad and *Mzee*
Omari, John, Shabani, and Charles, Africans who worked
with Dad at the slaughterhouse and the butchery in town.
Mzee Omari, being the oldest, sat in the front with Dad;
he had practically raised my father (I was told many times
by Grandma) and trained him in the art of cattle herding
and selecting. The bond between them was paternal, and I
could sense it when they talked or ate together, like father
and son. Dad addressed him as *Mzee*, the Swahili term of
endearment and respect for older men with wisdom. Even
though *Mzee* Omari worked for Dad, it always seemed the
other way round.

I climbed in the back of the Jeep with the rest. It was
partially covered with a faded tarp. I wanted the freedom
and adventure and the openness of the Land Rover from
which I could absorb the changing African landscape and
vegetation while driving southwards into the interior. Such
moments of adventure do not come our way easily. One
only reads about them, or watches them in some European
film about an exotic African safari. But I did not view it as
such. For me it was journey of discovery of new landscape,
new peoples.

In time, just before dawn, the Dhamani convoy left
Dar and headed west towards Morogoro, passing by shanty
towns in the distance from the main road leading out of
the city. The dawn light from the deep blue sky, with half-
moon, revealed the corrugated rusty roofs of the low cement
dwellings so common in African districts. Some makeshift
dwellings had kerosene lanterns suspended from the edge

of the roof, perhaps left outside from the previous night for the man of the household to make his way into the right household. A few African men, dressed for work, waded through the open field of dry red dirt towards the main road, as if dreading the idea (or perhaps hung over from the night before) of taking the early bus to their respective menial jobs.

I sat next to Charles. He was a talker, always deriding of people, and a heavy drinker of the local brew. Dad would often reprimand him when he came to work drunk, for his breath reeked of local brew, *gongo*.

But I enjoyed my conversations with him whenever I would accompany Dad to the slaughterhouse or spend a Saturday at Hasanali's butchery where Dad worked.

Charles said, "You see that house over there? That is where I stay, with all my girlfriends."

He then smiled, waiting for my reaction. He would always throw something at me, especially about girls, knowing that I had reached that age where I was curious and interested in girls.

"How many girlfriends?"

Charles said, boasting, "Oh many. I can arrange one for you, if you like."

I shrunk from embarrassment. Just then, Shabani told Charles to leave me alone. Shabani was an African Muslim, strict in his observation of the Muslim faith, the opposite of Charles, a free-spirited individual who lived day to day, relishing what little life had dealt him. Dad told me once that Shabani refused to handle pork or any meat scales on which pork was measured, yet Dad kept him for his loyalty and sincerity. So he became the kosher employee of the Hasanali butchery, and having acquired that reputation, all the Muslim patrons would go to him for service.

Shabani was a handsome man, well-built with an attractive physique — I always teased him that he looked like Muhammad Ali. He was married to an Arab African for five years, and already had five children.

After a moment, Shabani surprised me and said, "I want a second wife, an Indian wife this time. How come I cannot get an Indian wife? Why you people do not want us to marry your sisters?"

I did not know how to react, what to say. The question was beyond me and complicated, yet innocent, and beneath the naïveté was a profound social ethos of our society and its various races.

Everybody in the back laughed, stamping their feet and clapping their hands, as if Shabani had said something ridiculous. Even *Mzee* Omari chuckled from the front. Dad paid no attention; he kept driving.

As usual, Charles provoked Shabani, and said, mockingly, "Look at you. You might have a pretty face, but that is not enough. You cannot read and write. You have no money. You live in Kigomeni, under a hut. You already have a wife with five children. You think some Indian father is going to give his daughter away to some African worker like you?"

Shabani said, "The Indian father had no choice in Zanzibar few years ago. Maybe we should do the same here, force marry."

Mzee Omari, an illiterate man, yet of age and chiefly wisdom, intervened, as he always did to arbitrate rows between Charles and Shabani, and said, "No person should be forced against their will to marry, to work, to practice faith. It should be their free will and choice. Now you both shut up, or I am going to ask *bwana* Dhamani here to stop the car and let you both off."

Dad glanced at *Mzee* Omari, smiled, and kept on driving, leaving everything to the arbitrator.

Shabani and Charles both said, in unison, "Okay, *Mzee*, whatever you say."

Mzee Omari had the authority to bring calm over feuding workers at the slaughterhouse and the butchery. He had been around with the Dhamanis from the beginning, and carried with him an air of chiefly superiority. Dad would seek his advice on many occasions about dissenting workers, and he would negotiate with them and resolve the issue. He did not speak much, just his presence, like that of a village chief, brought emollient to mediation.

He was an old man but tall, lean, and strong. His yellowish, beady eyes spoke of wisdom earned, hidden pain from toil over the years, and a scrutinizing way to look at the world about him. He always donned the white Arabian cap (which many African Muslims wore above a flowing white *kanzu*) that covered his full graying curly hair.

We drove in silence passing large sisal estates on one side of the road. Dad and *Mzee* Omari talked in the front about herds of cattle grazing on the fenced farms along one side of the road, pointing and identifying the types of cattle.

After three hours of driving, crossing the Rufiji Bridge, passing endless stretches of large sisal estates along the way, we were approaching the outskirts of Morogoro town. We began our ascent along a hilly, winding road leading into the valley town. The morning clouds, like ruffled and stretched cotton balls, still clutched the summits of the Uluguru Mountains. The air was fresh and cool, without the oppressive summer humidity of the coast.

Along the dirt path, close to the road, women fully wrapped in colorful loincloths and full head scarves, walked steadily, carrying a bundle of firewood in one hand and woven baskets of fruits in the other; half-naked children followed them, happily. A few makeshift stands along the wayside sold fruits and drinks and *mandazis*; other vendors excitedly waved as we slowly drove past them. The ritual of waving by vendors lasted for rest of the way into town. It was a welcoming gesture for the newcomers.

Charles told me these were the *Waluguru* people. Their women, he said, are fine and beautiful, and always dressed in resplendent *kangas* and headdresses. The city people, as Charles regarded himself, thought less of them; they were from the interior, less urbanized, more traditional, and adhered to the old ways. But to me, their ways, closer to the soil and roots, were immensely rich and fulfilling, devoid of the conflicting demands of urbanization and tradition, so prevalent in the emerging metropolis of Dar. The migrant workers who came to Dar from the inland faced tremendous displacement; they lacked a center to revolve around.

The locals here were mainly pastoralists, rightly so, with the fertile and volcanic soils of the Uluguru Mountains providing the means of their livelihood.

As we approached town, the roadside became busier: cars on the road carried people into town from wherever and bicycles carried large basket of fruits balanced and tied in the back to the metal seat with sisal ropes. Along the road were a number of small and garish-colored cement dwellings with shoddy shop signs announcing their wares and a couple of petrol stations displaying scribbled signs of petrol price.

It was arranged in Dar by Grandma and Hasanali that the visiting party would be treated to a hearty breakfast, a feast at the local communal mosque, so we drove through the town center. On either side of the road leading into the town (and leading out as well) were small Indian shops with wide-open entrances underneath the awnings. From inside the dimly lit stores, behind the dusty glass counters, brown faces measured and greeted you with curiosity and suspicion.

In the center of town was an open market on one side of the road, and across from it, in the open uneven dirt patch, was a grand bus and taxi stand from where buses and taxis ferried their passengers to remote places. The bus and taxi stands were separated with potholed rows of cement islands and pavements from which, at equal distance, long black-and-white-colored poles with a small dusty metal sign on the top marked the destinations of the buses. In the background, beyond the pavement, were rows of small shops with loud signs: Kanji Clothing Ltd., Shah Enterprises Ltd., and Dewjee Tailoring.

The whole area was teeming and buzzing with men and women, waiting around their cargo of torn cardboard boxes secured by sisal ropes, chickens in bamboo cages, clay and tin pots of varying sizes wrapped in white cloth. Fruit and food vendors offered their goods for sale. From time to time, the sellers brushed off flies hovering over freshly-cut jackfruit.

We pulled into the mosque compound. Like all our communal mosques, it stood out as an architectural and dominant landscape, and surrounded by streets with shops and houses owned by community members. This pattern of building an existence around the mosque existed in all our cities and towns. It was a way of life around a center.

The receiving party was the *mukhi* of the mosque. The Dhamani brothers spoke with him, and we all were led into the dining hall, behind the prayer halls, where perhaps the communal festive occasions were catered.

Shabani said, "This must be your *jamatini*. Looks like the one in Kariako."

I nodded. His observation was spot-on. Our mosque had grandeur and presence in this rustic town: two stories with arched Moorish windows, a dome with a clock, distinct and conspicuous.

I followed Dad and *Mzee* Omari into the dining hall. Inside, tables and chairs were arranged for us. We were treated to hot tea, *mandazis*, hot *parathas*, and hot porridge.

Grandma seemed animated by the journey, but Mom was subdued, disengaged, as if she did all this out of duty and obligation. Other clan members talked boisterously at their table. The children were delirious with excitement. After a short while came the obligatory pleasantries, which always accompany these festivities, Kasamali thanked the *mukhi* for his hospitality and we set out again, heading southwest towards Iringa, stopping at the petrol station to fill up.

It was noon and the sun was overhead where it had burned away the morning misty clouds that had clutched the summit tops. Within minutes, I felt the dry heat stinging on the skin, burning the inside of my nostrils; it was different from the coastal damp heat. But the openness of the Land Rover and the rushing air from the drive mitigated the discomfort.

Iringa was a long ways off, another four to five hours of climbing the treacherous roads along the ridges of the central plateau. Dad and *Mzee* Omari had made this journey previously. The Iringa highlands had rich pastures for grazing, and many African cattle herdsmen raised their cattle on these high plains. Beef from this region, according to Dad, was premium quality.

The four-hour drive to Iringa was mostly in low gears as we ascended the plateau and the vegetation got denser, grass thicker along the roadside, the air slightly cooler. Now and then, we drove past Africans walking along the red dirt path by the roadside, sometimes waving. Excited children ran barefoot along the path, waving until the convoy proved too fast for them to keep up. Dad drove with one hand on the wheel and the other – its bent elbow pointing outwards – along the edge of the rolled-down door window.

Outside Iringa lived an Arab cattle supplier from whom Dad sometimes bought cattle. He was informed of our arrival. Tucked away on the highlands was a cattle farm that belonged to Musa bin Ahmed. The open barns with corrugated roofs were close to the main farmhouse, and you could hear and see the cattle moving about behind wooded enclosures secured with ropes. Next to the barn was an open area where cattle grazed. It reminded me of the slaughterhouse outside Dar: the manure stench, the constant mooing, and the buzzing flies.

Hasanali, Kasamali, Dad, *Mzee* Omari, and Musa bin Ahmed went off to the barn, perhaps to select and discuss the next shipment. I went to see Mom and my brothers inside the main farmhouse.

The farmhouse was a rusty cement dwelling with a corrugated roof, half-dozen rooms, and high, strong ceiling beams. Our host had his family – five children of all ages, young adults, and two wives – all living together under the same roof, perhaps in different rooms. They were kind and welcoming, and offered us their kitchen to heat up the food that we brought along, and the bathroom to freshen up.

In the Arabian way, we all sat on the floor in a circle, cross-legged, and ate with our fingers from the large silver plates of food in the center. Women talked and mingled about in the background. Grandma rested on the comfortable sofa, and talked with the hostess. After a hearty meal, *kahawa*, black coffee, brewed in a conical brass flask, was served in minute cups for drivers who were going to drive for the rest of the night. Our host offered to let us spend the night, but the Dhamanis insisted that would delay us. Hasanali said they wanted to arrive at the Malawi border by morning.

Outside, the sun left behind its fading glow. The highlands were silhouetted, and at dispersed locations on the far-off hills, flames from the kerosene lanterns in the African huts and outside evening wood fires flickered like ambers of charcoal. The evening air was cool, the early evening stars appeared just above the horizon.

Dad suggested to Charles and Shabani that they cover the tarp and secure it in the back. He asked me to put on a sweater and get a blanket from the suitcase.

The clan members in the mini-buses seemed tired. The idea of the long night's drive began to take its effect on them. They yawned as they boarded the buses. We bid our farewell to the hosts and set off into the cool evening towards the Malawi border. After wading slowly through the dirt path out of the farm, we were back on the tarmac road, and shortly, the African interior darkness engulfed us like a blanket. Only the powerful headlights of the convoy guided us.

I was delirious with adventure, peering outside through the front windshield, looking for anything. We were now in the African wilderness, miles away from town. There were no villages with their lanterns and wood fires anywhere in sight, only darkness behind us, and only beams of light from the Land Rover illuminated the road in front of us.

Charles said, "If we get a puncture, we are a feast for the wildlife. The lions and hyenas will have to fight who gets to eat Shabani."

Mzee Omari said, "Charles, you smell of pork ribs, I think they would go for you first."

232

Shabani clapped in excitement at *Mzee* Omari's retort. Charles remained quiet after being cut by *Mzee* Omari.

The convoy traveled slowly and cautiously along the winding ascent and descent as we approached the high altitudes of the Rift Valley. Dad said that on one side of the road is a deep plunge. This part of road towards Mbeya and beyond, he explained, had claimed its share of lives. Once you go down, there is no way to rescue you: the plunge is your burial grounds.

Fear of adventure gripped me as I peered in front, watching the brake lights of the mini-buses ahead of us. Dad seemed comfortable and secure at the wheel. He shifted gears and steered with the confidence of a veteran safari driver. I admired him as he handled the Land Rover with his will. There was no fear of accidents; everybody on both buses was a seasoned driver. The Dhamani brothers, before they became proprietors of the meat enterprise, had made these journeys in the interior, driving refrigerated trucks carrying slaughtered carcasses. This was familiar territory.

My mind wandered into the past as I thought of what secondary school history had taught me. This was the tribal region of the Wahehe; their chief Mkwawa, a ferocious leader, as the books described, had led the *Maji-Maji* rebellion to fight and overpower German colonization several decades ago. With his charm and leadership, he had convinced his warriors that sprinkling the water from the African soil's river on their chests would turn German rifle bullets into water drops. And merely with that invincible conviction of immortality and primitive weapons — spears and pangas — he led the guerrilla warfare for several years in and around these highlands, until one fateful day, an overpowering German contingent surrounded his rebel group. Rather than being captured alive, the proud chief took his own life. The Germans then beheaded him and sent his skull to Germany.

I tried to imagine the battles fought in the jungles of these highlands: the German soldiers slaughtered with pangas, the rebels cut down with machine-gun fire, their belief that the bullets would turn into water a charade. But it takes such conviction to fight, to dissolve the fear of death. The German soldiers were told Africans were savages; the dehumanization of your enemy is what propels warriors and soldiers to slaughter.

Such casual brutality amidst this serene mountainous landscape was painful to fathom. But behind these serene landscapes, monuments and wonders of the world, lies an ugly and brutal buried past. Always unpleasant remnants of history are buried or altered, some for convenience, others out of shame and self-hatred. Yet it is the responsibility of the writers and historians, to record such passages of the past, however unpleasant.

Around me, Charles, Shabani and John had slumped into slumber of exhaustion. *Mzee* Omari and Dad talked and sipped *kahawa* from a thermos our hosts had given us. With Dad at the wheel and *Mzee* Omari awake and by his side, I felt secure, and slouched on the floor, covering myself with the woolen blanket. In moments, the monotone noise of the Land Rover engine receded and I gradually slipped into the dark void of sleep.

We had stopped when I woke, and outside the sun had risen, bright and golden. We were at the border crossing between Malawi and Tanzania. The official harassment by Malawian authorities had commenced. The borders were fairly open, people traveled freely between the countries; no wars had yet broken out, and most countries were in their early independence years: Nyasaland became Malawi after independence two years ago. The British colonial influence still remained strong and prevalent. And the Malawian president, Dr. Hastings Banda, maintained strong ties with his colonial masters, as well with the neighboring regimes of Rhodesia, Mozambique, and South Africa.

When the border patrol officer, dressed in colonial uniform – khaki shirt and shorts, blue-knee-length stockings, and polished black shoes — came around the Land Rover to inspect, he addressed everybody in English, with affected superiority, and asked mundane questions.

After he was done with us, he walked languidly towards the bus.

Behind his back, Charles said, "I would never have my sister marry that African. He is ugly and very black, like charcoal. This is the interior. Not like the coast. Africans on the coast are lighter and prettier. Look at me and Shabani. Or you, *Mzee* Omari. You are old now but still look good."

Mzee Omari said, "You think you are better than them?"

Charles exclaimed, "Yes, I am superior to them!"

Mzee Omari shook his head in disappointment. He thought of saying something, but refrained; perhaps it was not worth his effort. Charles, he might have thought, has problems. Even at work, he always derided his clientele from the interior, always made fun of them, and mocked their accent.

He called Abdul, the Indian driver, *kasuku* (parrot) because of his prominent hooked nose. He labeled the Indian woman from across the street from the butchery who insisted that the scales be washed before weighing her meat as the "bow-legged witch," and the frail Punjabi woman next door to the butchery who begged for discarded bones for her mad dog "*mama umbwa*" (mother dog), or the man

235

with the long face who delivered eggs at the butchery "*uso chupa*" (bottle face) and the Indian woman with a large distended stomach who brought cold water for Dad at the butchery "*mama mtungi.*"

Such were the grotesque labels Charles had attached to his clientele. We were accustomed to this casual cruelty uttered in street banter — it was not unique to Africans, but pervasive in Indian households, between husbands and wives (verbal tirades), between fathers and children (beatings), among boys of different Indian sects (street fights), between school teachers and students (punishments); its roots lay elsewhere.

Kasamali and Hasanali walked with the border patrol officer to the administrative offices: two cream cement buildings with glass windows and wooden doors. Outside the building, just a short distance away from its entrance, was a large circle made of white bleached stones, and in its center a small mound of dry dirt from which emerged a flag staff, hoisting the Malawian flag, a common colonial landmark of the officialdom in the interior.

After a while, the Dhamani brothers and the officers emerged from the office building, laughing and shaking hands with the immigration officers. Some matters were solved, perhaps a bribe was asked for and the request was granted, and our convoy was given the go-ahead to enter Malawi, the country within the African Rift Valley along the long and narrow Lake Malawi.

Just past the border patrol, in the open area was a restaurant that welcomed tourists. A few Europeans sat outside the tables and gave us curious looks. Our men went inside to fetch some tea and we all ate our Indian snacks with tea at the tables farthest from them.

Certainly, this was high country. The air was crisp and chilly when a faint breeze blew from the east. In the far distance, the gentle slopes covered with lush vegetation rose to high altitudes. A lingering morning haze gave the green slopes a distant out-of-reach appearance.

When Dad returned from the toilet, he looked exhausted, his eyes red, from driving through the night, and Hasanali suggested that he rest in the bus while Abdul *Kasuku,* one of the backup Indian drivers on the bus, take over the Land Rover for the journey up to Blantyre.

The plan was to drive into Blantyre, the capital city, and spend the night at a hotel, then carry on the next day for Salisbury, our destination. A good night's rest will do everybody good, Hasanali suggested.

All my life, I had never spent a night at a hotel. That concept was alien to me, as there never was a need, up until now, to do so in the visiting country. There were always relatives' houses in the towns we visited, or a communal guest house to sleep in. The idea excited me.

And with that plan, after breakfast, the convoy resumed its voyage southward along the narrow country to Blantyre. The road was busier than expected, mainly tour buses and cars, with holiday makers, dominantly Europeans, a few Asians, going northward to the shores of Lake Malawi.

All along the way south, we saw evidence of rich, fertile soil from the Rift Valley: lush vegetation of scrubs and tall Savannah grasslands, stretching for miles until it merged with woodlands at the slopes of the plateau. A few tall trees with spindle-like foliage emerged like lamp posts along the roadside. During the dry season, the Savannah grasslands turn golden, providing perfect camouflage for a pack of hunting lionesses, entrapping the grazing gazelles and wildebeests.

I asked Abdul, "Where are all the animals? We have not seen any."

Abdul said, "They stay away from the road. They remain deep inside the jungle, far from the roads. And most of them live within the boundaries of game parks. Most don't like cars and the noise they make.

"But if you go off the main road, like that dirt road up there about few miles inside, you may see them. I would not dare," Abdul chuckled.

In the far distance, rain clouds gathered, and in a matter of time, we drove through sheets of pouring rain, hitting us at an angle. December was part of the rainy season here. Even during the day, in the far distance above the slopes, you could see dark, ominous clouds gathering, then a bolt of lightning and brilliant flash slicing across the clouds and zigzagging through it, tracing into the ground at the horizon, followed by rumbling thunderous noise, and then the downpour.

In this open space of grasslands, these acts of nature evoked a sense of awe in me, and I sensed the rest in the Land Rover felt the same. We drove in silence for a few hours until we reached a small roadside town, where we stopped. The rain had ceased, but remnants of the recent downpour were evident around the roadside town: little rivulets of water running on the side of the road; the fruit stands damp; the foliage in the tree dripping; the trickles of water from the ends of the corrugated roofs; and the fresh red mud in the soil.

We ate fruits: bananas, oranges, mangoes. Charles and Shabani went off to a small open hut where dried fish from the lake was being cooked on an open grill, and next to it clumps of meat and beef ribs. Dad bought me some grilled meat on a wooden skewer. He knew his meat well.

The Africans here spoke very little Swahili, but we managed to communicate. The local dialect was Chichewa, and sounded much like Swahili.

Blantyre was a large city with broad boulevards and arching street lamps and tall buildings and wide two-way roads. Like Dar, it was the commercial center, and like it, all the commercial buildings, banks, and government offices were centered on several major streets in town. Other parts of town, on narrower streets, had rows of identical shops, some owned by Indians, others by Europeans – Greeks, British and Portuguese.

The European hotels were in the posh areas of the city, perhaps inaccessible to us. We sought a hotel owned by an Asian in the less posh area of the city. A petrol station owner, an Asian, provided directions to it.

Mr. Mukerjee owned a large guest house and a restaurant in town, not far from the town center where we stopped to fill up on petrol. He provided for us five large rooms at a low cost, Dad told us later. Our family had its own room. For dinner, we ate delicious Indian food at the Kajal Restaurant adjoining the guest house. After dinner, the men disappeared, perhaps went drinking, and the women went to their respective rooms. My brothers went to sleep with Grandma, and I went to play cards with *Mzee* Omari and Charles and Shabani in their room.

The room walls were bare, painted in garish yellow color, with chintzy curtains and wooden tables and beds with mosquito nets. The floor had a grimy checkered plastic carpet, torn and curling up at the edges where it met the walls. A small ceiling fan swirled above us, and a tube light on the side wall illuminated the room.

This was not my idea of spending a night in a hotel. I had other images of it: air-conditioned rooms, plush dining areas, expensive-looking lounges with upholstered chairs, swimming pool, uniformed waiters and polite hotel attendants. It was a borrowed and an elusive image from the scenes in the cinemas. Such privilege was not for us. It was for the rulers, people with power and wealth.

In time, I left for my room. Mother was still awake, turning the pages of the local newspaper, which showed picture of Dr. Hastings Banda visiting a local hospital.

Outside, I heard faint sounds of cars honking, people talking, women laughing, and African music flowing from the bar down the street, where everybody was flocking. I was curious to visit the bar, to see the African women dancing and drinking.

When I was playing cards, and while *Mzee* Omari stepped outside for a cigarette, Charles said, teasingly, "Hey, want to go to the bar with me? I can get us two young Malawian women."

I was aroused by the prospect of what would have transpired if Charles and I sneaked out at night, but suppressed my imagination and fell asleep. I was awakened by intense moments of pleasurable sensation between my legs, as the muscle spasm in my throbbing penis ejected sticky fluid — I had a wet dream.

Once more, we were on the road, after a sumptuous, characteristically Indian breakfast – purees, curry potatoes and vegetables, and masala chai — at the adjoining Kajal Restaurant. Mr. Mukerjee had brought his family and introduced us. The Asians here, a small, tight-knit community, much smaller and more segregated than ours — were curious about other Asians elsewhere in the newly independent countries up north. The conversation invariably revolved around business prospects in the newly independent countries and the future of Asians in Africa. But much, I reflected, would depend on us: our adaptation to the changing political climate, our ability to thread the middle road, and our desire to participate in the political and civic process of our respective new nations. Was our survival in our hands, or in the hands of those who will rule?

The road out of the city threaded through large boulevards, side and narrow streets jutting out from it like river tributaries. A large roundabout with lush garden and blooming flowers at the center of the main boulevard in the city had numerous zebra-striped arrow-sign posts, indicating directions. Major African cities' names were printed in black with their distance in miles from the city. It gave Blantyre a sense of importance: the city from which every other city was accessible. The Salisbury sign read: South 375 miles.

Africans, dressed smartly, walked briskly on sidewalks. The morning activity indicated purpose.

Charles peered outside, taking interest in women smartly dressed in western attire, wearing nice shoes and carrying purses, their hair tucked in neat headdresses.

Charles said derisively, "Office workers during the day, whores at night. I bet if I went to the bar, I would see them tonight."

Mzee Omari retorted, "Your sister in Dar is an office worker. What bar does she go to? Rex Hotel?"

Everybody in the Land Rover chuckled at the exchange, even Dad managed a smile. He probably heard this all day long at work: Charles squawking abuse at patrons after they departed, and *Mzee* Omari cutting him with his sardonic replies, while the rest of the staff enjoyed the verbal duel between them.

The road narrowed as we left the city, and miles ahead, it became rougher, slowing our pace. We had to cross

Mozambique to get to Rhodesia, past the Tete Corridor, across the majestic Zambezi River, through the long patches of red dirt and mud huts, different in structure from ours. This southwestern part of Mozambique seemed barren: no roadside stops of fruit vendors, no Africans waving and walking along the road path, no sign of villages along the road: just endless stretches of red earth on both sides of the potholed road. I feared any car malfunction. But we were prepared.

Mr. Mukerjee in Blantyre had suggested we carry extra petrol and had given us plenty of food to last us to the Rhodesian border. He had admonished us not to stop at desolate road junctures, and not to drink any water from river tributaries. This portentous advice introduced a sense of adventure and drama. For the rest of the way to the border crossing with Rhodesia, all of us in the back just peered outside at vast red earth passing alongside us in silence for hours.

As we approached the border crossing, there was no sign of guards at the Mozambique section. The two small dingy sentry stations and a low cement building were deserted; the wooden post gate was raised, and a dusty wooden sign read in Portuguese and English: Leaving Mozambique.

The Dhamani mini-buses ahead of us stopped at the gate, honking to summon officers, perhaps sleeping, in the low cement dwelling. The sun had set, and it was dark inside the office which looked unoccupied. Shabani alighted and went to inspect, and returned, saying there was no one at the station. Satisfied, we crossed the border.

A few yards ahead of us was the Rhodesian border crossing, illuminated with reflecting signposts, and the cement office buildings were lit up with naked bulbs outside. The lanterns of the two sentry huts were suspended from hooks outside. Alsatian guard dogs sat menacingly at the sentry hut doorway.

As we approached, two Africans dressed in official khaki uniforms and a white officer, sullen and stern-looking, used flashlights to signal us to park our cars to the right.

The Dhamani brothers and Dad got out.

The white officer asked sternly, "Where you coming from?"

Kasamali said, "From north, Tanzania."

The white officer said, "Where are you going?"

Kasamali said, "Salisbury. We are having a family reunion of relatives we have not seen for many decades."

Kasamali then fumbled and produced a large official affidavit of papers that Shamshoodin Dhamani had sent, along with the invitation, vouching for us as his guests for a few days at a farm outside Salisbury.

The African guard whispered something to the white officer. And judging from what happened next, I reckoned it was about the Africans we had on the mini-bus and the Land Rover.

"Who are those Africans with you?" asked the white officer, as if annoyed.

Kasamali produced our Tanzanian papers and the work documents of all the workers who were with us. He said they all were employees of the meat enterprise he owned back in Dar.

After fumbling with the papers and studying the mini-bus, he said with superiority, "We have rules in this country. Africans and Indians are not allowed in various public places in the cities. We do not treat you foreigners any differently. Be mindful of that. Do you understand what I just said?"

Kasamali, familiar with colonial and apartheid polices of former colonies, now independent, said diminutively, "Yes, we will respect the laws of the host country. We are only going to the farm."

The white officer's mannerisms were deliberate and acquired towards non-whites.

Then he barked some commands in the local dialect to the African sentries. They leashed the guard dogs and led them to sniff the convoy. Inside the bus, women screamed as the dogs sniffed about; the dogs picked up the scent of old dried blood but ignored it. Perhaps they were trained to recognize the scent of something else: drugs or ammunition.

There was more control and authority at this border crossing than all others we had passed. Which race was in control was unequivocal. To a visitor, the taste of racial division was stark and overt at the outset. Here, within minutes, I sensed an ingrained and legislated policy of racial division, just like what we had during the early days of colonial rule.

Kasamali asked, "How far to Salisbury?"

As if annoyed and burdened by the simplicity of the question, the white officer said in a muffled voice, without looking at him, "Follow the signs on the road."

As the Dhamani brothers approached the convoy, they both spoke in Kutchi and Swahili, cursing the white officer in common deriding terms.

Charles added his bit and said, "Our *Mzungus* are better."

The women and children in the bus complained of fatigue and they wanted to use the bathroom, but the signs outside the office buildings for the bathroom read: "For whites only." Behind the cement building were two makeshift toilets which were reserved for non-whites. Instead, we drove up the road to a safe clearing and went to the bush.

Ahead of us, the full tarmac road sank and rose in the headlights of the car, and my stomach felt the falling sensation with each dip and rise. Small reflecting road signs appeared on the side of the road at intermittent intervals. Finally, a green road sign read:

Salisbury 250 ml
Mutoko 63 ml
Glendale 325 ml

At night in Mutoko, the yellow streetlamps revealed a small, quiet town with small cement dwellings, orderly small gardens, and clean narrow streets, deserted at this hour. Insects revolved around the dimly lit streetlamps. Most hotels along the main road were shut. This was a mining town, closer to the mining region of northeastern Rhodesia. The surrounding townships provided the cheap, exploitable African labor for the industrial mineral deposits.

We parked outside a bus stop area on the side of the main street. An empty bus with marked signs on its side, Johnson Mining Transport, was parked at one of the bus stops. Other narrow streets off the main road were dark alleys, and I feared what lurked there. The Dhamanis decided to rest until dawn before the last leg.

Faint voices outside and the running engine of the parked bus woke me. Only Shabani was slumped next to me. Outside, the blue and silver light of dawn edged the receding darkness. Birds chirped from the nearby trees, and in the distant background, a hen crowed. We could have been in Iringa or Mbeya; these remote African towns had familiar characteristics: central bus stop area with a market space across from it; shops along the main street, and narrow alley-like streets off it; and the early-morning human traffic of Africans departing for their menial jobs.

Across from the bus stop, a small café's doors were open with people walking in and out. Its outside tube light illuminated the asphalt, where I recognized *Mzee* Omari sitting at a table, sipping tea. Next to him was Dad, and inside seated at the table were men from our convoy. The café was owned by a portly Asian man; most of his patrons were Africans eating their breakfast before a long, laborious day at the mines.

Within minutes, the Dhamani clan descended onto the café and occupied much of it, denying some of its daily African patrons any seating. The Asian owner was welcoming and effusive, and like Mr. Mukerjee in Blantyre, curious about us. He asked familiar questions, as though it was an established protocol of pleasantries among us. This had become an expected pattern of conversation with Asian encounters in these southern African countries. And it lay at the bedrock of our uncertainty and lack of conviction and confidence in the prevailing political climate; some of it stemmed from our own ignorance, and absence of historical pride and achievements for the continent.

Some moments later, we set off for Salisbury in the bright morning light. Along the road, townships appeared in the distance, and farmlands in the foreground, carved neatly in rectangular patches of crops, stretching along the roadside. Now and then, a narrow dirt path off the main road led into the distant farmhouse: a sprawling red, brick cement building with cottage-like roof with shingles. At the juncture of the dirt path and the main tarmac road, English names marked the ownership.

Dad said, "This is the longest journey I have ever taken in my lifetime. Something I will remember."

Mzee Omari said, "There is always something for each of us to learn from this journey."

Indeed there was. We had traveled for three days, longer than we had anticipated, depended on each other for support and comfort.

Salisbury began to reveal its clustered satellite African townships of corrugated-roof houses of red bricks. Traffic became dense with buses ferrying people into the city. Cars driven by whites competed with buses and trucks on the road leading to the city center.

In time, we entered the sprawling city: tall buildings with glass windows, manicured and tree-lined wide boulevards, large stores and shops along the major streets, imposing colonial structures of government administrative buildings, glamorous hotels, roadside cafes and restaurants.

The country's wealth from mineral resources and the world-dominant tobacco industry manifested itself in the splendor and grandness of Salisbury. It had the draw and feel of a modern city, a European city in Africa.

It was steeped in white privilege. Everywhere on its streets, white women dressed in their cotton frocks walked the sidewalks, African nannies behind them, pushing the baby prams, or carrying groceries. It was segregated at every level of function.

We stopped at a petrol station to fill up, and at the non-white-only counter, Hasanali asked the directions to the farmhouse address on the papers sent to us. He bought the map from an Indian-looking man behind the glass counter, who seemed affable. He knew we were non-locals, and out of affection – and partly because we were Indians like himself

– gave us precise directions to the farmhouse by outlining the route on the map.

The farmhouse was more than half an hour's drive outside the city. Along the road to it were large farms — tobacco, maize, millet, sorghum and other crops – owned mainly by white settlers. Beyond all the settlers' farms, at the end of the paved road, isolated, was a narrow entrance to a dirt driveway. At its entrance, a tall wooden sign board, hanging like a flat pendulum, read: "Shamshoodin Jamal Dhamani, 17 Drake Road, Salisbury."

The dirt driveway led to a large clearing covered in gravel so that approaching cars made a grating noise, announcing their arrival. Beyond it was a large red-brick farmhouse bungalow with bay windows and wooden door. To the right of the bungalow, a short distance away, was an open barnlike garage where tractors and other farm machinery were parked.

The gravel area had numerous cars with local registration numbers and a couple with South African registration plates; we added ours to the mix.

The grating sounds of the gravel from our convoy brought out the excited receiving party: the mysterious other Dhamanis. Who was who, only time will reveal. But when the Dhamani brothers and Grandma got out of the bus, it was apparent who our host was.

Shamshoodin was a large man, bolding and portly; he wore the large farm overalls to conceal his large belly.

"Oh, Gulbhanu Bhen," he said affectionately, and hugged her, his voice cracking, and then he hugged the Dhamani brothers, and finally after all the lengthy introductions were finished, we went inside the well-furnished farmhouse. The women spent time getting acquainted, the men sat around the large living room, drinking, the alcohol mitigating the initial awkwardness of painful acquaintance.

Mzee Omari walked past the farmhouse and went behind it. He knew where to go; others helped with the luggage. In time, Charles, Shabani, and John were mingling with the local workers at the farm, trying to communicate in broken English.

Behind the farmhouse were the servants' or workers' quarters. Their family lived here with them: children, wives, grandmas, sometimes brothers and sisters. Some African men worked on the farm, others around the house, and their wives helped as nannies or maids or cooks.

I met Iqbal, my distant relative from Durban; his father was Pyarali Dhamani, who had driven from South Africa. Iqbal was a year older than me and had finished his matriculation. And he had an older brother, Feerose, who had finished his second year, reading law, at the University of Natal in Durban. He was reticent, but warmed up when we spoke later. They both spoke English with a very distinct South African accent, and so did Shamshoodin and Pyarali Dhamani, but with traces of Indian and Afrikaans.

Later in the day, outside by the barn, as we walked, exploring the surroundings of the farmhouse and escaping the family boredom, I asked Iqbal while Feerose walked alongside, "So what is next for you after matriculation?"

Iqbal said, "I very much want to study medicine at Witts. I have the marks, but not sure if I can be admitted. They only allow a few coloreds and Indians."

I said, "What are your other choices?"

Iqbal said, "Go where Feerose is at University of Natal. But it is very political. I hate politics."

Feerose said, "You have no choice but to expect politics in a country like ours. Politics shape and touch every fabric of your life. From cradle to graveyard, your life is shaped by what race you are. It is naïve of my brother to think otherwise."

"You feel South Africa is your country?" I directed the question at Feerose.

Iqbal rolled his eyes, suggesting contempt and inevitability of yet another futile political discussion of race and citizenship. The futility of such discussions and the despair was perhaps the motivations for Iqbal's desire to flee from Durban.

Feerose had formed a strong political identity with South Africa. He explained to me the history of Indian activism, since the days of Mahatma Gandhi, in the Natal province in the late 1800s, and how even today, after a century, through various Indian political organizations, they fight for Indian rights. Such passion for political activism, eloquently narrated by a distant cousin, inspired me. I wondered whether all Indians his age from wealthy families of merchants and shopkeepers felt the same.

Feerose said, "Regrettably, not all of them. But the ones attending the universities are getting influenced when they become the victims of the policies.

"There is no denying that some shopkeepers and merchants have benefited from the apartheid system, but the poor majority side with the Africans all the way."

The time I spent with my reunited peers, it was an indication (an illumination of sort) to me that the course of history for Indians in the south was markedly varied from up north. And it was that course of history that had forged their identities and political aspirations far different than ours. We in the north had it easy. Our contribution to the struggle for respective countries' independence was limited and marginal. What was achieved was diminished or marginalized as not worthy of mention in the history books.

But here in the south, history spoke for itself: the immense influence of Indians in politics of Natal and with the present formation of the liberation movement taking hold in the country secretly.

That history, albeit not mine, yet of people of my heritage on the southern continent, made me proud to be an Indian in Africa. And bit by bit over the days I stayed at the farmhouse, I began to form a strong sense of the Dhamani history through Shamshoodin and Pyarali Dhamani: what their grandfathers had endured. But nothing came from it about our side – that bit was gone.

Although the Dhamanis from the south had climbed the economic ladder of racial politics, their humility touched me. I only hoped that our Dhamanis from up north could learn a lesson from this meeting of parted clans.

On the day of the departure for the arduous trip home, a tragic comedy unfolded in the backyard. My two younger siblings – Faisal and Jamil – woke up early that morning and went outside, behind the farmhouse, into the courtyard. In the center of the courtyard was a well, encircled by raised red-brick masonry. A leather-torn football lay at the foot of the brickwork.

Faisal said, "Let's play football."

He kicked the ball to Jamil, and they passed the ball back and forth. After a short moment, a chimpanzee appeared from under a tree behind the servants' quarters and languidly walked towards them. He grabbed the ball and rolled it to Jamil.

Jamil looked at the chimp, and then looked at Faisal, amused.

Faisal said, "I think he wants to play football with you. Go ahead and kick the ball to him."

So Jamil did, and the chimp caught the ball like a goalkeeper and rolled it back to Jamil. And Jamil kicked back. This rally — Jamil kicking the ball, the chimp diving and catching and returning the ball — continued for a short bit until Faisal teased and prompted Jamil: "What is your problem, you cannot score against a chimp? Kick harder!"

So Jamil kicked harder and harder, and with each kick, the chimp deftly caught the ball and rolled back, pounding his chest and showing off his decaying teeth and pink gums.

Jamil was embarrassed by such overt showmanship by the ape, and he kicked the ball with all his strength. The fast ball hit the chimp hard on the face and threw him flat on his back.

It was an act of aggression. The chimp got up and charged at Jamil and pounced on him, throwing Jamil onto the ground on his back, with the chimp on top of him, biting, punching, and slapping Jamil with his large curved, furry hand.

At first, Faisal thought it was all amusing, but then realized that Jamil was terrified; the chimp was beating him, drawing blood from Jamil's face and arms. Faisal ran to fight the ape that had attacked his younger brother. He kicked the chimp several times, as hard as he could, but the chimp would not let up. He then wrestled the chimp off Jamil's chest and told Jamil to run to the farmhouse.

Instead, Jamil, shocked and bloody-faced, ran around the circular brickwork. The chimp, arms in the air, puffing and pounding his chest, chased Jamil; and Faisal chased behind the chimp. Round and round they went several times, all three shouting and screaming.

The commotion in the backyard brought about from the servant quarters an old African lady, who shouted at the chimp, and the chimp ran towards her. She slapped him and chained him to the tree.

The chimp was a local pet around the farmhouse, raised since a little baby, and the children around the servants' quarters had taught him to play football.

The old African woman then ran inside to fetch the Dhamanis. At first, Dad laughed, and then realized the gravity of Jamil's inflicted injury. They had to rush him off to the nearby clinic. Hours later, Jamil returned, bandaged up like a mummy.

To date, whenever I see my brother, I remind him of this incident, and he has never forgiven Faisal for the provocation.

The long journey south marked us all in many different ways, and as *Mzee* Omari had said early on, we each had learned something about ourselves.

Glossary

askari - A night watchman or a guard.

banyas – A derogatory term for Hindus.

bhai - Gujrati or Kutchi word for brother.

chokra – A child or progeny in Kutchi

dadima – Grandmother in Kutchi.

darkhana – A mosque located in downtown of any large town or district.

gujarati – A dialect of Indian language spoken in the state of Gujarat in India.

haraka – A Swahili word for hurry up.

iti-dandi – A game, played mainly in Indian districts of Dar by youngsters, with a small wooden stick, sharpened at both ends, and a small bat used to hit the stick.

jamat Bhais – A man or a caretaker for the mosque who lives and works in the mosque.

Jamatini – A Swahili word for an Ismaili Muslim mosque.

jungbari – Someone from the coastal islands – Zanzibar, Pemba, or Kilwa, and having a unique and poetic style of talking.

kabisa – A Swahili word for affirmation.

karibu – A Swahili word for welcome.

kanzu – Arab African white cotton robe often worn by people on the coastal and interior towns along with the Arab white hat. Most African and Arab Muslims wore it.

kahawa – Strong and concentrated coffee commonly served in miniature cups. Popular drink around coastal towns among Africans and Arabs.

kidari – Beef ribs.

kikapu – A small basket woven together with dried leaves.

kitenge – A colorful African printed cloth from which dresses or shirts are sometimes cut. Normally, African women wear it around their waist, over a dress; sometimes it is wrapped around the shoulder and used to carry small babies.

khojas – Indian Muslim Ismailis who were converted from Hinduism in India. Many of them came as merchants and traders after the first initial wave of indentured workers to Africa and organized themselves socially, commercially, and professionally.

khuda – Gujrati or Kutchi word for God.

kuku-paka – a rich and delicious yellow thick coconut curry chicken dish

kutchi – A dialect of Indian language spoken in the state of Kutch in India.

kushali – A festive occasion celebrated in the mosque.

mandazis – Deep-fried leavened bread, a breakfast dish for many Africans and Indians.

mbuzi – Goat meat.

mbwana – A Swahili word used to address someone, like sir.

miskakis – A Swahili word for meat delicacy: small pieces of spicy and marinated meat, threaded with skewers, and grilled on an open charcoal fire.

mpaka – A Swahili word for a house cat.

muhindi – A Swahili impolite term for Asians in East Africa.

mukhi – A leader at the Mosque who leads the morning and evening prayers and conducts communal religious rituals.

mrungus – A carved and polished wooden stick from the strong branch with a large bulb on one hand; it is usually used as a striking weapon by African warriors.

mzee – Swahili term of endearment and respect for addressing an old African man.

mzungu – Swahili for a European.

nyama – Meat in Swahili.

parathas – Indian bread cooked in clay oven.

pangas – A machete.

sardaji – A Sikh who mainly wears a turban.

takhat – An area in the Ismaili mosque with large picture of their imam to which prayers and money are offered. Its use now is deprecated.

uchavi – African black magic.

unguja – The island of Zanzibar.

ya ali – A greeting common among the Ismaili Muslims.

Printed in the United States
67755LVS00001BA/1-48